ALSO BY A. C. GREENE

A Christmas Tree
Dallas: The Deciding Years
Dallas U.S.A.
Elephants in Your Mailbox (with Roger Horchow)
The 50 Best Books on Texas
The Highland Park Woman
It's Been Fun (with Jake Sandefer, Jr.)
The Last Captive
Living Texas
A Place Called Dallas
A Personal Country
The Santa Claus Bank Robbery
Texas Sketches
A Town Called Cedar Springs
Views in Texas

TAKING HEART

A. C. Greene

SIMON AND SCHUSTER
NEW YORK · LONDON · TORONTO · SYDNEY · TOKYO · SINGAPORE

Simon and Schuster
Simon & Schuster Building
1230 Avenue of the Americas
New York, New York 10020

Designed by Sheree L. Goodman
Manufactured in the United States of America

10 9 8 7 6 5 4 3 2 1

Library of Congress Cataloging in Publication Data
Greene, A. C.
    Taking heart / A. C. Greene.
        p.   cm.
    1. Greene, A. C.—Health.   2. Heart—Transplantation—
Patients—United States—Biography.   3. Journalists—United States—
Biography.   I. Title.
RD598.35.T7G74   1990
362.1′974120592′092—dc20
    [B]   90-34044
                                                                              CIP

ISBN 0-671-68392-6

The ideas, procedures and suggestions contained in this book are not intended
to replace the services of a trained health professional. All matters regarding your
health require medical supervision. You should consult your physician before
adopting the ideas, procedures and suggestions in this book. Any application of
the treatments set forth in the book is at the reader's sole discretion and sole risk.

Parts of this book originally appeared in *Dallas Life* magazine of *The Dallas
Morning News.*

To Betty, who owned both my hearts

A new heart also will I give you,
and a new spirit will I put within you;
and I will take away the stony heart . . .
and I will give you a heart of flesh.

Ezekiel 36:26

HEART: a hollow muscular organ of vertebrate animals that by its rhythmic contraction acts as a force pump maintaining the circulation of the blood, is in the human adult about five inches long and three and one-half broad, of conical form, is placed obliquely in the chest with the broad end upward and to the right and the apex opposite the interval between the cartilages of the fifth and sixth ribs on the left side, is enclosed in a serous pericardium, and consists as in other mammals and in birds of four chambers divided into an upper pair of rather thin-walled auricles which receive blood from the veins and a lower pair of thick-walled ventricles into which the blood is forced and which in turn pump it into the arteries, back flow being prevented by valves. . . .

HEART: the whole personality including intellectual as well as emotional functions or traits; memory, rote, opinion, attitude, posture; the emotional or moral as distinguished from the intellectual; conscience, character, spirit, generous disposition, sensibility, compassion, feelings; temperament, disposition, mood; goodwill, willingness, sincerity, zeal; love, affections, courage, ardor, enthusiasm, taste, liking, fixed purpose or desire; ardent wish; intense concern, solicitude, or preoccupation; one's innermost being, one's innermost or actual character, disposition, or feelings; the central or decisive part of something; an essential part, the part that determines the real nature of something or gives significance to the other parts; the determining aspect; the center of activity; a vital part on which continuing activity or existence depends; core.

—*Webster's Third New International Dictionary of the English Language, Unabridged, 1981*

Acknowledgments

This is a survivor's journal, about a survivor's journey and how I think one can join it. I had not realized I was a survivor. I had chalked it up to luck, skill, intelligence—a survivor knows better. No one factor, not even luck, can do it. The survivor survives, and that's all he does; he doesn't worry about how well he survives or if he should or shouldn't be doing something—he survives on persistence, and I hope that's what this book will help readers perceive. The survivor throws away regrets, scares, fears, and obligations, and sticks to one goal: making it. This is a book about surviving that most ominous threat to life: the attempt on one's life by one's own body. "Things have a way of working out" becomes a useful philosophy, nondogmatic, a survivor's creed.

This book was written with the cooperation of several surgeons, cardiologists, and other medical professionals but was not written with their authorization (except where personal expression or direct quotes have been given) or at their behest or incentive. Its ideas are purely my ideas, and it is purely my choice of words, examples, and observations.

It is not intended as a medical guide or to refute any side of the ethical questions that arise concerning transplantation (and there are quite a few). It is merely the reaction, the very human reaction, of one very human person. I do not offer my experience as a standard by which to measure anyone else's experience or as a basis for making medical decisions. I may praise certain medical personnel who have worked with me and on me (quaint phrase!), but this is not to be taken as a recommendation of any approach, process, or medical opinion, or the work of any physician or medical personnel involved in the growing transplant field.

However—and I say this not in defense but in explanation—I have found since my own transplantation that certain fears, misgivings, questions, emotions, and interior feelings seem to be common to all potential transplant patients and those near them. I have listened to transplantees, watched stories on film and video, read articles and books by and about them, and have said to myself many times, "Yes, that's the way I felt, too." So the purpose of this book is to offer a human interpretation of the whole transplant experience—in my case, the heart transplant, the most dramatic if not the most difficult of all transplant operations. I have tried to keep from preaching—cross my heart—but there is so much to say beyond the relating of events, events that in many instances began as medical experiences but turned into spiritual demonstrations.

I have tried not to employ too many medical deductions, only personal ones. For years my profession has been expressing myself, and while I may not do it any better than most people, I do it more frequently; therefore, I'm more inclined to start the process than others might be. Many books about medicine are written from an expertise I don't have—but mine is written from experience.

If you are expecting a book of downsides, don't read this one. Plenty of downsides are presented, but upside balance can be wrapped up in one phrase: *otherwise you die.* I didn't talk to health professionals about this downside/upside business. I talked to me. Despite so much medical bureaucracy that too often tries to treat problems by pattern or computer model, every case is its own. In life there are fewer patterns and more variables. Chance and coincidence, which I once rejected, I now can see become realities. Creative writing teachers warn students not to solve fictional problems with coincidences, but life does it all the time. There is no such thing as coincidence, it's merely juxtaposition: 1 and 1 can be either 2 or 11.

This isn't so much a book about escaping death, despite numerous references to surviving, as it is a book about finding life. It is a book of ordinary virtues, not miracles, except for the paramount miracle of existence. I'm very dramatic, but is there anything more dramatic than living, than waking each morning to the uncertain proposition that you will make it through the day, that the drama will continue for three acts, that the show will not end with the first curtain . . . or the second or the third?

I wish to thank Dr. William L. Kraus, the transplant team of the University of Texas Southwestern/St. Paul Medical Center, and all the people who so graciously and successfully wrapped me in their care during the many months I was crossing the heart transplant spectrum from one end to the other. The team included, in my case, Dr. W. Steves Ring, Dr. R. P. Cochran, Dr. Larry Pass, surgeons, Dr. Terry Latson, anesthesiologist, and Marcy Estes, perfusionist, of the transplant team, and Dr. Aaron Estrera and Dr. Cochran, the donor retrieval surgeons. Nancy Johnson, R.N., was Chief Transplant Coordinator and Kathy Srokosz, R.N., was Nurse Administrator and Interim Transplant Coordinator. Allison Ballew, R.N., was Southwest Organ Bank Donor Coordinator. Cardiologists included Dr. Vernon Horn and Dr. Brian Baldwin, as well as Dr. Kraus. The Coronary Care Unit nurses paid so much attention to me when I was in their care that I felt like a celebrity. I owe my life to all the above, and what other fact should solicit more gratitude?

My thanks also go, in profusion, to Roxanne Fall, St. Paul Medical Center Social Worker, who helped my family through not only my period of trauma but, later, my wife's. Patricia Kaiser, R.N., joined the transplant group as Transplant Coordinator shortly after my operation and continued to herd me along toward survival. Nancy Buckley McNally, R.N., Sarah Little, R.N. (my favorite nurses in the whole world), and physiologists Lee Hampton, Cynthia Gibbons Atkinson, and Aaron Day, Jr., were leaders of the cardiac rehabilitation program who made workouts a pleasure instead of labor. Alberstein Myles's skill in the blood lab saved my nerves through a hundred (so far) visits.

I would not want to leave the impression that the University of Texas Southwestern/St. Paul Medical Center transplant program is the only one or the only successful such program in Dallas. Although mine was the first adult transplant under their program, it was not the first successful adult transplant done in Dallas. In March 1989 surgeons at Baylor University Medical Center in Dallas, where several successful heart transplants had been done, also performed the first "domino" transplant in Texas. A good set of lungs and a good heart were taken from a brain-dead donor (who had suffered a fatal gunshot wound) and put into a man with a good heart but a congenital chronic lung disease (the operation works best when donor heart and lungs are transplanted together). The heart-lung recipient's good heart was in turn transplanted to another man with good lungs but a failing heart. At that time fewer than ten such domino transplants had been performed in the United States.

I made use of several books, especially Mark Dowie's *We Have a Donor* (St. Martin's Press, 1988), Lee Gutkind's *Many Sleepless Nights* (W. W. Norton & Co., 1988), and Norman Cousins' *Anatomy of an Illness* (Bantam Books, 1981). *Heart Corps* magazine, which was still in volume one when I was writing this book, furnished several interesting quotes and ideas.

Special thanks go to Diane Reichsel, who graciously allowed me to use anything she had written about me, and John Ashby Wilburn, who furnished a title for this book after its author had struggled with fifty or more entries. And to Judy Greene, whose editorial assistance carried me through several rough revisions. Robert Asahina was the editor who contacted me before my transplant operation and suggested I might write a book about it—with the subtle understanding, of course, that I would survive. He turned out to be a genius taskmaster who saw the finished product more clearly than I did.

Chapter 1

The last thing I remember as I was being wheeled into the cardiac operating room of St. Paul Medical Center in Dallas on June 27, 1988, was someone telling me it was 7:55 P.M. I heard my daughter Meredith say, "We kissed him, so do you need to spray him down with that brown stuff?" And a nurse laughed and said, "No, we'll leave your kiss . . . *that* kiss." I heard my wife Betty say, "He looks beautiful," and then, after a pause, "But just think how much better he's going to look." Meredith said to her mother, "He's going to look even more so better," then to me, "Well, next time we see you, you won't all be there, thank goodness."

I had been waiting at the hospital since three o'clock that afternoon, but those waiting hours had passed without leaving too many tracks on my memory, only pale traces of nurses and technicians appearing, counting, poking, then disappearing, and these vague, unrelated snatches of conversation at the end of an in-and-out-of-consciousness trip on a stretcher. I had entered the hospital so weak and collapsed that I immediately fell asleep and time passed unnoticed or unremembered through what I am told were reams of tests. There was a brief arousal of being loaded on a gurney and shepherded by family and nurses through halls, down unfamiliar corridors (along which I floated rather than rode) to that set of ominous operating room doors, hearing those last good-byes, and through those doors, feeling the burst of light in the operating room—then more sleep.

I woke from that sleep wondering where I was. I was coming out of a nap, I felt, not a sleep of any duration, but I recognized nothing that I saw. My surroundings were unfamiliar. There were no friendly signs to indicate where I was. I heard voices. They sounded strange. I tried to turn. I couldn't lift my hands. I couldn't move my legs. I was tied down. Restrained. My God! Gradually faces appeared. First Betty's, then my daughter's. Both were smiling.

I tried to speak but could only whisper: "When are they going to do the operation?"

"It's finished," my wife said.

"Finished?"

"You have a new heart!"

And much the way an unexpected comber breaks over you at the seashore, suddenly I heard sounds of life swirling around me: the music of voices and words, communications from the world that I had been out of for nearly two days (I later discovered). Finished? A new heart? In me? I must have stared, inwardly if not outwardly. I'm not sure I believed. A new heart. I sank back again in sleep.

Many hours later, emerging through a lingering fog of anesthesia into a truer ability to recognize what had happened, I awakened in a hospital room. My ankles were no longer tied, but I bristled with tubes, wires, catheters, and machinery—injecting or withdrawing fluids, measuring my life in heartbeats, pulse rates, blood pressures, internal statistics . . . all the things needed to be kept track of, minute by minute, to assure my continued existence.

A nurse appeared from somewhere, smiling.

"Where am I?" I asked, a traditional query of the postoperative patient.

"You're in the Intensive Care Unit," the smiling nurse said.

"What day is it?" I asked, another traditional query, I'm told.

She smiled again and said, "Well, it's not exactly day, it's night. It's Wednesday night."

"And I'm still alive?"

"You're very much alive. In fact, we've been waiting for you to wake up so we could tell you how alive you are. You're doing just great."

"How do you know?"

She laughed. "We can tell every move you make, inside or out, from our monitors. That's why I came in. You made an unusual move—you woke up."

When she left me, I did a mental inventory of myself and my situation: I felt no pain, although I couldn't move sufficiently to discover if there might be jabs and burning spots on my body. The soft restraints remained on my wrists, but I was elevated enough so that I could see my chest was heavily bandaged and wires led from various points around the edges. The restraints were to keep me from pulling out any of those tubes and wires. Meredith said later that when I was first being wheeled into ICU, I was making pen stroke motions with my right hand—a natural reaction for a writer, she felt, not my trying to pull out some vital tube. She thought the nurses should have given me a pencil and pad.

I asked myself how I felt, afraid that in my wonder at waking I might have overlooked some pain or some gnawing ache of the body. My mental inventory was still a bit muzzy, but the part of my mind that was functioning was assuring. I might not know where I was or what day it was, but I knew how I felt: wonderful! Through the fuzziness of remembering came my wife's words, "You have a new heart."

I wanted to try it, I wanted to put my hand over it and feel it beat, to check my pulse as I had done so many times a day back in that long-ago age (it seemed now) when I was struggling to keep my old heart alive. The restraints, the bandages, the wires conspired to keep me from feeling the beat with my fingers but not with my imagination. A new heart . . . a new heart. Somewhere in a nearby room bright points of light were dancing across a monitor screen, spelling out my life-beat if not my name: Greene's new heart . . . Greene's new heart . . . Greene's new heart.

A new heart, a new start, a new life? I thanked God I was alive—the very thought making me joyously happy. Not merely happy but overwhelmed by the growing realization that I had successfully undergone one of the most extreme and fantastic medical procedures of the twentieth century. My bad heart had been taken out and discarded, and the good heart of another person had been inserted, made to operate, and was operating efficiently in its new home. I had a heart, and regardless of how many more years awaited my happier fate, nearly ten years of questioning and uncertainty were over.

When full realization came to me, when I convinced myself I was through it, and the realization and the moment were mine without sharing, I started crying. It had been years since I had shed tears for myself. I suppose my last tears had come from the death or memory of someone and their time, the sort of tears a man should shed without caring who sees or knows that tears are being shed. Maybe if, in the first place, I had shed more tears at more of life's changes, I would have laid less of a burden on my heart—or if I had let my emotions have that moment when some passage at a concert swept my heart strings or a line of poetry moved me or a remembered scene from a film renewed its initial passion. If . . . if . . . romantic *ifs*. But the tears I was shedding in that strange, unfamiliar room were tears of a different sort, tears of joy, thankfulness, and release. With each wave of emotion I was washing away some of the cynicism, the peevish wounds I had nurtured in my old heart, the unimportant worries and frustrations that had accompanied me, even unconscious, into the operating room.

New heart, new start, and—I was determined—a new life.

Chapter 2

That tearful moment of realization was the climax of a long, twisting journey I had begun nearly ten years before, a journey of life and death and the heart: my life, my death, my heart. It began one morning when I received a casual telephone call. My friend Dr. William L. Kraus, a longtime Dallas cardiologist, invited me to visit his new office and try out his new equipment: new treadmill, new electrocardiograph (EKG) machine. "I've even got new running shoes for the treadmill," he said, adding diplomatically that there would be no fee. As the cliché goes, it was an offer I couldn't refuse. And thank God I didn't.

I wasn't worried about taking any physical tests. I knew I could be energetic, even capable of sustained vigor if called on, despite the fact that the calendar of my daily life showed leaves that were more sedentary than strident. I'd spent years as a reporter, editor, freelance writer; I had taught university classes and been a radio and television performer (do I begin to sound like a club act?). In general, I had pursued vocations that kept me active but seated. However, I knew I was healthy, especially for a man my age, which was mid-fifties.

As a young man I had been fairly athletic, playing reaching and jumping sports such as baseball and volleyball. As a boy I'd ridden a one-speed balloon-tired bicycle, laboriously pumping across town with two full newspaper bags lapped around my neck (the big Sunday edition almost choking me). Three years of active duty with the United States Navy and Marine Corps during World War II had found me firm (and unwounded) at the time of my discharge. As I had gotten older I hadn't turned soft and flabby, but like most American men who remember (or think they remember) how energetic and strong they were as boys, every so often I would start some kind of physical exercise such as bicycling, calculated to regain that lost youthfulness and get my pulse pounding.

During one period I played a lot of cartless golf (I couldn't afford to rent a cart), and I became involved in badminton on a weekly basis with a troupe of fine players—so fine that in a vicious singles game I pulled a leg muscle and ended my badminton career. Even at age forty-five or fifty I worked on and off at elevating my pulse rate. Not jogging or long-distance running; I was more inclined to do five hundred counts of running in place or a dozen situps on the bedroom floor—those mornings when I could take time.

But I was not too concerned about physical examinations. I had no potentially dangerous family medical history, no childhood disabilities apt to revisit, no nagging chronic ailments, no leftover bouts with illnesses that threatened to return. Oh, a little overweight (sometimes by 20 percent), but my stomach didn't hang over my belt—if I stood up straight and sucked in. You just have a big frame, I said to myself when occasionally viewing those pounds in a full-length mirror.

Very healthy, I was convinced, especially my heart. And why shouldn't it be healthy? I didn't smoke. Never had a cigarette in my mouth, as so many of my nicotine-enslaved friends had heard so many times. As for diet, I was never much of a salt eater, save on fresh-sliced tomatoes and egg dishes. I didn't overindulge in eggs, either . . . unless I was staying at the Sagebrush Inn in Taos or some other southwestern spot where *chiles rellenos* (made with rich egg batter) could tempt a dietary saint into transgression. And despite having raised four children in the television age, I eschewed "fast foods," and because as a child I had squirmed at the way one of my kinfolks used to eat pure fat, I always trimmed the fat, although I never became alienated from red meat.

My alcohol consumption was marginal, seldom more than a drink now and then—a Dos Equis beer or two with Mexican food or some Tsing-tao beer with Chinese food (after all, I'd spent nine months in Tsing-tao with the Marines, living in the same compound with the brewery). Hard liquor? I wasn't in much demand on the cocktail circuit, and at my age barhopping was not merely inappropriate, it was indecent. Oh, one well-constructed martini with my wife on the patio at dusk, the evening sky turning dusty gold, then fading to star-spangled night—but that sounds like *three*-martini talk!

Ice cream? Well, everybody has to have *one* weakness, and my wife's homemade vanilla or peach was the only ice cream I glutton-ized in, if you insist on calling six or eight bowls gluttony. Summing up my condition and attitude, while I did not try to deny my human vulnerability, I didn't get too concerned over it. I shared a trait with many males: health smugness.

So it was with light step and lighter heart I appeared in Bill Kraus's office for the proffered workout and examination. On the treadmill, wearing a pair of those new running shoes, I urged the technician, "Give me a hill to climb!" As the EKG leads were attached to my chest and limbs, I felt complacent-to-gloating . . . and inside my head, congratulatory. After all, how many men in their fifties dared match heartbeats with me? Even famous athletes my age that I read about, with their arthritic joints, their broken bones and torn mus-cles, drew my sympathies if I made physiological comparisons. And watching overweight, middle-aged joggers lumbering along the resi-dential streets every morning or circling through air-conditioned shopping malls during a Texas summer, I thought how glad I was that I didn't have to be one of those poor devils in sweat suits, watching his diet, wishing he'd never seen a pack of cigarettes, alarmed at the cholesterol and sodium content of everything from spring water to tofu desserts. Like the biblical Pharisee, I self-right-eously thanked God that I was not as other men are.

Of course, as I lay there that morning being measured electroni-cally by the machine, I had to admit that running on the treadmill *had* pulled a lot of energy out of me—I hadn't approached hill height. And now that I thought of it, on some days life seemed to sit on me pretty heavily for no reason. But frankly I made acceptance of weariness a concession to age: Mother Nature reminding me that I would never see twenty or thirty again. Nothing more. As the EKG clicked and whirred and the printout rolled forward, I felt unruffled. The old ticker was strong and steady.

When I was dressing again in street clothes, Bill came to my cubicle and said he wanted to see me in his office. I knew why: Congratulations were in order. I was a marvel of well-preserved mature manhood. In his new office he waved me to a leather chair, the electrocardiogram with all its squiggly lines in hand.

"A. C.," he said rather solemnly, "I want to show you something."

But of course, he wanted to show me how good and regular my heart worked. He pointed to several curlicues along the EKG tracings. "You have a heart problem," he said, and didn't smile.

A heart problem? I asked him again. The answer failed to change. I had heart trouble. He went into more detail, something about arrhythmia or an irregular heartbeat with postventricular contractions. "Arrhythmia alone we might just live with. Lots of people do who never develop other coronary symptoms," he was saying, "but those PVCs are something else. They make it dangerous." He explained that PVCs were uncoordinated contractions by the ventricles of the heart that, if uncontrolled, could result in the dread state of ventricular fibrillation, which means total loss of circulation—and sudden death.

But shocking as this was, I was only half hearing him. My mind was still resisting his first statement, "You have a heart problem." Who was he talking about, and what did he mean, "heart problem"? Was he getting his information from that EKG printing he was looking at? What did some machine know about me that I didn't know better? And even if he was a Harvard-trained physician, why would my friend Bill Kraus take the word of those wavy EKG lines before mine? These thoughts flew through my brain for several unbelieving moments, then my reluctant better judgment took over and I recognized what a panicky reaction I had had. Of course the EKG knew more about my heart than I did, and of course the machine had to be believed. I was not unfamiliar with the EKG, having worked in a hospital as a young man (and knowing, as all the young know about themselves, that I was immortal and that EKG results applied only to the aged—people past thirty). And I admitted that Dr. William L. Kraus knew more about hearts, mine included, than I could hope to learn, although at that moment who would have predicted that I might, in the next few years, learn so much? A heart problem? I could have cried right there, and almost did—but stout-hearted men don't cry, do they?

Subduing the shock of recognition, I settled down internally and, as calmly as possible, asked what he recommended. Bill said he thought a mild form of medication should restore regularity to my heartbeat and control the PVCs. A few days later, after he had done X-ray studies of my heart and chest and found no enlargement of the heart, he prescribed a certain drug, which I began taking three times per day. Convinced at first that I was under a death sentence which must be commuted, I tried not to acknowledge the predicament, thinking there had to be a way out or that I might by some feat of integrity, such as denying it, vanquish this sudden new enemy. Time smoothed my acceptance (with reservations), and even though I still told myself I was like a visitor in a foreign country who knows he will eventually return home, I convinced myself to follow the specific rules and do as I was told—since I was just visiting. The medication had no side effects on me, and within three weeks my heartbeat seemed back to normal.

But that first frantic day, I was depressed, fearful, embarrassed. I didn't want to admit I had a bad heart, not even to my wife. I waited until bedtime to tell her, then I tried to make it seem like a casual suggestion Bill Kraus had made rather than a serious charge.

"Did you do your treadmill test with Bill?" she asked.

"Un-huh," I replied, as though the event had been uneventful.

"Is that all, just 'un-huh'? Did he find anything?"

"Nothing really. A little irregularity in my heartbeat."

"Well?" she said, giving me that wifely gaze any long-married man understands to mean, "I know better."

I still wanted to hide the bitter truth. "He . . . suggested I take some capsules, a mild medication. To control the irregularity."

"Let me have the prescription. I'll get it filled first thing tomorrow."

"I've already had it filled. Here." I exhibited the plastic container, and I got another wifely gaze. She knew. If I had thought it was serious enough to get a prescription filled immediately, it was serious. After the lights were out and we lay in the darkness, I admitted all—all, that is, except my fear. I didn't want to appear fainthearted.

Chapter 3

After I got over those first days of apprehension, the three-times-per-day medication routine grew automatic. My condition eventually became so normal that, with the doctor's approval, I cut down to two pills and sometimes only one. Every six months or so I went back to Dr. Kraus for an examination, EKG, X rays, and blood work, to make sure the medication was still holding. For a long time it *was* holding. Every time we met socially the doctor in him caused Bill Kraus to reach casually for my wrist and check my heartbeat. A thumbs-up gesture generally followed, and I'd feel smug again—especially for a man my age. I forgot I was supposed to have heart problems, and sometimes I forgot to take my medication. (Bill wouldn't have approved, of course, but since no distress resulted and I didn't let it happen very often, I felt it not worth mentioning.) The main things Bill warned me about were using too much salt, going out in the noonday sun and overexercising. Since exercising (or doing much of anything) in the noonday sun had never been my inclination—not since age twenty-five, at least—I found no sweat (forgive the pun) in his admonition.

Another thing Bill Kraus was concerned about was my weight. I wasn't noticeably fat, but the extra pounds were there, adding to the burden my belabored heart carried through every beat. I tried most of the palliatives the undisciplined overweight patient offers himself. When I weighed as much as 210, I stopped weighing, telling myself that it was a momentary thing, that I would be over it before I weighed next, and there wasn't any point in disappointing myself with such a weight. But sometimes it took weeks to lose as many as three pounds, and I never got below 200 pounds until disaster in another form faced me. Then *overweight* took care of itself, and weight *loss* became the problem.

Thus, for well over a year I assumed I was protecting myself solely against angina pectoris, the severe pain and constriction around the heart that darts to the left shoulder and down the left arm, and myocardial infarction, or blockage within the coronary arterial system. Of course, like most people who have been warned they have a heart problem, every little twitch or jerk in certain parts of my body caused at least a *mild* flutter of fear: Was this the beginning of an attack? I discovered that was not necessarily going to be the case one midsummer night when Dallas heat had been going up the temperature ladder, leaving 100 degrees behind. Although I was in an air-conditioned bedroom, I began having trouble breathing. I'll just elevate my torso, I told myself, but when I added a pillow to the one I was using, I found it did no good.

This had been one of those "good" days when I had not taken my medicine, even one pill, so I got up and belatedly did so, returning to bed confident the oversight was taken care of. It wasn't. By 1 A.M. I was forced to sit up fully in bed or not breathe. And when I say "not breathe," it was exactly that. For the first time in my life I had to force myself to breathe, to remind myself to suck in, push out. My heart and lungs simply were not doing it automatically.

"What's wrong?" Betty asked.

"Nothing," the macho-stoic said. But she knew better. She turned on the bedside lamp and gave me another of those gazes. "You've been snorting and panting all night. What's wrong?"

"I forgot to take my pills. I did just now, and that should take care of it."

"Just now? I heard you get up and take your medicine hours ago."

"It's no big deal," I said, resorting to teenage dialogue. "I feel better." She hesitated but believed me and went back to sleep.

(Wives are not *always* all-knowing!) Next morning the symptoms seemed to have passed, and I took a vow never again to overlook or delay my medication. I went back on three pills that day at specifically prescribed intervals and swore that would always be the case. That night, after another scorching day, the heart's performance (or lack of performance) of the night before was repeated. This time I didn't try to circumvent it with more medication but sat bolt upright in bed throughout the night. Betty, who had bought my whiny defense of the night before, was having no more of the macho-stoic business. (She and Ann Kraus, Bill's wife, had entered into a wifely conspiracy to see to it that I shouldn't try to brave things out.) As soon as daylight appeared, Betty called Bill Kraus at home, handing me the phone. I told him about the last two nights and he said, "You're going to the hospital." I was relieved he had not even *asked* if I felt like going. I had reached the point where I gladly surrendered any right to say.

In the hospital I had two days of testing and treatment: all kinds of X rays, heart scans, lab work, giving every kind of specimen the flesh is heir to and having a heart catheterization and coronary arteriogram (during which an X-ray camera shows the condition of heart arteries when an opaque dye is injected via a tiny arterial catheter—and hits you with a penetrating warm jolt). I noted with delight, as I lay on the cart and watched the monitor screen, that my arteries were clear and vivid. "That's good," I told myself. "I don't have heart disease."

I was right and I was wrong. No, I didn't have coronary atherosclerosis (a form of arteriosclerosis), the most common type of heart disease due to hardening of coronary arteries. The arteriogram and other testing confirmed this. But the tests found I had something with a milder sounding name but just as inauspicious: cardiomyopathy, a chronic disabling of the heart muscle that usually leads to congestive heart failure. I learned this was a gradual condition in which the heart can't maintain adequate circulation. "It's good news and it's bad news," Dr. Kraus told me. "Good news in that you probably won't have the pain of a heart attack. Bad news because the usual treatment of heart problems—bypass surgery, valve replacement, angioplasty [use of a tiny balloon to clear clogged arteries], or a pacemaker—won't help your condition." Why not, since my heart on the monitor appeared so good? He looked grim: "Your heart," he said, "is dying. We can keep it going, but we can't stop the process."

At that point I dropped all pretensions of manliness, normality, and lack of fear. I now recognized mortality—that condition we exist in from birth but don't acknowledge for so many years. And I was scared and didn't deny it.

Like most men when they discover they have a heart problem, I wondered how long it would be before I was confined to a wheelchair or to my bed, destined never again to jump, climb, run, or charge hell with a bucket of water. My heart, my good, strong heart. What happened to you, heart? Where did I go wrong, and why have you let me down? You, who I thought was my best and closest friend. I have told you everything, heart. You know all my secrets, all my joys and fears; you have shared my elation and depression, my unexpressed infidelities and professed faithfulness. No keeping from you the lust of the flesh, the pride of the eye, the wrath, envy, gluttony, avarice, sloth that passed in and out of me: You have been privy to it all. And now you have failed me.

To a mature male, especially one who has never had any severe diseases or disabilities, his heart is his pride. His heart *is* the man. Look at how society, since caveman days, has characterized its finest males: stronghearted, Richard the Lion-Hearted, "Give me some men who are *stouthearted* men. . . ." And what did the Tin Woodman lament in *The Wizard of Oz?* ". . . if I only had a *heart!"*

What do we value most? We value the heart; the heart is the dearest thing we own. "Take my heart . . ." we say in poetry and in music when we want to offer our most precious gift. Can you imagine someone singing, "Take my liver . . ."?

"The heart of animals is the foundation of their life, the sovereign of everything within them, the sun of their microcosm," said dear old William Harvey, the seventeenth-century English physician who proved how important the real (as opposed to the metaphysical) heart is when he announced the blood's circulatory system. No computer will supersede Dr. Harvey's deposition. The heart will always belong to poets and musicmakers. Just as man walking on the moon has not rendered moonlight ineffective or unbecoming, so the transplantation of hearts, even if the day comes when something other than human flesh is doing the circulating, will not make us surrender our passionate feelings about the heart, our conviction that, despite surgeons, science, and wonder drugs, the heart is the heart of the matter—the matter of life.

In the Bible when King Saul's life was changed, it says, "God gave him another heart." The psalmist asked, "Who shall ascend into the hill of the Lord? or stand in his holy place?" and specified, "He that hath clean hands and a pure heart." Christ, facing death, reassures his Apostles, "Let not your heart be troubled, neither let it be afraid." A change of heart implies we've straightened our twisted lives. We've employed the heart politically: It beats with truth and righteousness. A national presidential campaign in the 1960s suggested that even if one hadn't planned to vote for a certain candidate, "In your heart you know he's right."

And look at our language. One of the meanest things we can say of a person is that he or she is heartless. Coldhearted equals ruthless. A pallid or hopeless gesture is made halfheartedly, by someone whose heart "isn't in it." Lose your heart, even in love, and you lose control. Envious? We mock: "Eat your heart out!" And when we aim to persuade, we say we must win hearts and minds equally.

We humans are urged to "take heart!" To accomplish anything, "ya gotta have heart!" Even children recognize the heart's importance in matters of conviction and integrity, promising "cross my heart and hope to die" as pledge of truth and righteousness. But the heart is more than the center of human pride and strength. It is the mystical as well as the mythic center of existence. Heart and soul are inextricably mixed in phrase and fable. Where the heart is, we have persuaded ourselves for eons, there will the soul be also. In Bartlett's *Familiar Quotations,* Heart has nearly as many entries as Life, Love, and God. All the heart terms make it, in popular belief, even more important than the brain: "A man's heart deviseth his way. . . ." So when a man discovers he has heart trouble, he feels terribly lessened, put down by fate, and he can't understand what or why. Myth and history have elevated the heart so that a man with a bad heart feels almost guilty for not being the stronghearted male or having the "heart of a lion" or any of the other terms history has applied to so many forceful figures.

To tell a male he has heart trouble attacks him in his manhood, and doubly so at an older age when inherent masculine assets already are waning. First he denies to himself he has a problem, then he wants to hide it. Sterility is sometimes voluntary and impotence is often curable, and in any case these deficiencies can remain secret virtually throughout a man's life, but not heart trouble. It can be embarrassing. Some men would rather risk death than admit they are having heart trouble. And some men die.

On average, women seem to take the news of heart trouble better. Females are less vulnerable to pride of strength. After all, they are considered, by tradition, to have more delicate hearts, hearts more easily "broken" by mere words. Society may expect women to be internally strong, but whoever heard a musical chorus sing, "Give me some *women* who are stouthearted women"? Simply being male also has a lot to do with the fear and loathing of coronary atherosclerosis. From age thirty-five to forty-four, for instance, the death rate for males with the disease runs six times that of females. On the other hand, one imagines the discovery of severe heart problems in a man somewhat parallels the discovery of breast cancer in a woman, an attack not only on her pride but on her gender identity. Of course, no one, male or female, wants to be told he or she has heart trouble, and it is as disturbing medically to a woman as it is to a man—but the stigma (imagined or not) of the clay-footed idol doesn't adhere to the female as it does to the male.

Chapter 4

Like most people, when I read about a dramatic scientific advance, I take it for granted that some huge human problem has been solved, or at the very least, everything about the problem has become known. Thus, it came as a shock to the average heart patient such as I was, thinking of myself as well informed, to discover just how much remains unknown about a thing as ancient, pervasive, and daily as heart trouble. I assumed there would be some magic medicine or some marvelous laser tool of some sort to wrap up my weaknesses and deliver them marked "Cured" after, oh, say, six weeks . . . six months?

To me, heart trouble was heart trouble. You got a pain in one side or the other of your chest, it shot down your left arm (or was it your right?), and if you got to the hospital or an ambulance got to you in time, those masked magicians passed a scalpel over your heart, shot some kind of miracle drug into your veins, maybe did a bypass (whatever that involved), and had you working as good as new or maybe even better than new because (as the medical writers chided) you had finally waked up to your situation.

So it was alarming, unnerving, and scary to find that I had a heart problem, not only a heart problem but one that little or nothing could be done to cure. Only a few measures that might "take care of things for now"—an alarming medical prognosis. What saved me from panic was not stoicism or self-control, it was ignorance of my particular situation. And fortunately, by the time my ignorance quotient was diluted with a little more knowledge, I had learned enough to keep a fairly calm if not altogether resuscitated heart in my chest.

I would not attempt to make a thorough medical description of heart trouble, but since there are many kinds and since most of us conceive of "heart trouble" as making itself known only by shocks and "heart attacks," I will try to sort out some of the differences we don't know or think about until we are staring down the barrel of the gun.

Most of us imagine the heart's only job is to circulate blood, pumping it out through the arteries and back through the veins, if we recall that much high school biology. But one of the heart's main jobs is to keep the lungs clear of excess fluid. The good heart circulates blood through the hairlike capillary vessels of the lungs at low pressure to pick up oxygen from the air we inhale. When, for reasons known and several not known, the heart muscle gets too weak to pump out the lung's fluid, the fluid-level pressure in the heart cavity and in the lung capillaries rises, fluid leaks into the lung's air sacs, and blood oxygen can no longer be kept up to standard. Congestive heart failure (congestion caused by this excess amount of fluid) is the general term to describe the falling down of the heart's pumping function. Dropsy, that ancient edematous disease we've read about in the Bible and so many Victorian novels, is almost always a form of congestive heart failure in that it indicates an excess of water in tissues, water that a healthy heart prevents from accumulating. Thus, even with clear arteries and no blockages, a heart with muscle degeneration (cardiomyopathy) gradually dies.

What causes heart failure or cardiomyopathy? We seldom know. What can or could have been done about it? (These were the first questions I asked, of course.) Unfortunately, there is little that can be done medically once the heart is scarred (the usual cause of muscle degeneration), and there is seldom a precaution that even the best trained cardiologist can offer or an event a doctor can point to and say, "Ah, here's what caused it." Sometimes cardiomyopathy begins with an unnoticed viral infection, and the heart is scarred without the victim so much as having had to take to the sick bed. Sometimes a childhood illness, which left no discernible disability, strikes years later. A congenital defect or an inherited weakness can lead to heart failure, but even that is unpredictable. Many researchers now believe stress contributes to heart failure, but patterns of such are still emerging from medical studies. Diet may or may not have something to do with heart failure, but the general feeling is that, save for sensible dietary precautions that apply to all hearts, it is negligible. As for exercise and stimulation, in cardiomyopathy cases they can do more harm than good. Heart failure also strikes young as well as older persons. Every fall, you read about some young high school or college football player collapsing on the field and dying of heart failure before being carried to the sidelines. And in most of these cases the young athlete had undergone a presumably thorough medical examination before starting to practice or play.

I also discovered that coronary artery disease, such as coronary atherosclerosis, is quite different from heart failure like mine. Coronary artery disease is what so many of us have trained meticulously to avoid by cutting down on, giving up, or avoiding tobacco, alcohol, fats, cholesterol, salt, and sugar, and taking up running, jogging, bicycling, handball, racquet ball, walking, and other aerobic exercises that work up a sweat.

And as anybody who can read or hear knows, there is the question of cholesterol: Is it all bad, is it bad for everyone, is it bad for *me?* The *Journal of the American Medical Association,* which in general takes the position that a high cholesterol level is bad, estimates that 60 million Americans above age twenty have cholesterol levels high enough to put them at risk for coronary disease. The *Journal* reported finding the average blood cholesterol level for the adult American male was 211 milligrams per deciliter (mg/dl) and for the female it was 215 mg/dl, both counts being high, especially in younger persons. We shop for low-cholesterol or no-cholesterol ingredients, but our national averages will probably persist at those levels or higher as long as we eat so much processed food.

All the cholesterol taken in as part of one's food is not bad; in fact, some cholesterol (LDL, or low-density lipoprotein) is good. And not all doctors and nutritionists condemn cholesterol outright in heart problems. There are exceptions to the rigid rules of "this much and no more" that allow some professionals to question the ultimate role of cholesterol in heart cases. If cholesterol is a risky ingredient (and I'm not hinting it isn't), the real enemy is saturated fat, forming HDL, or high-density lipoprotein. Replacing saturated fats in a diet with polyunsaturated fats such as safflower and corn oils or (even better) monounsaturated fats such as virgin olive oil and canola (rapeseed) oil may even lower cholesterol levels. Cholesterol's danger comes not from merely consuming cholesterol-laden foods but from your body's inability to handle the cholesterol overload so that instead of being refined, processed, and used by your body, it becomes saturated fat, which is the primary agent in artery clogging. The lowering of liver functions is why the older you get the more likely such clogging (or coating) will build to dangerous thicknesses. We may know people who virtually live on saturated fats and survive well. What's the answer? Apparently their organs can handle the load better than most people's organs, the way some eighty-year-olds see well without glasses and some ninety-year-old hearts tick along stronger than some forty-year-old hearts.

A recent study done by the National Heart, Lung, and Blood Institute (which the insurance companies listen to attentively) reports that for every 1 percent reduction in one's total cholesterol levels, a 2 percent decline is rewarded in the risk for developing heart disease or having a coronary attack. Bring down your cholesterol levels by 25 percent, and your coronary disease risk is cut by 50 percent.

Some three-fourths of all Americans will have some sort of atherosclerotic lesion by age thirty, even if it has not blocked the arteries. So while controlling cholesterol is a problem for nearly all of us, the ability to utilize the "good" LDL cholesterol to offset the "bad" HDL takes some of the burden off the consumption aspects of the problem if we are observant. Close attention to what we are eating, reading labels, and knowing how much saturated fat and other "nonos" foods contain are major answers. More and more discoveries and developments along this "good versus bad" cholesterol product line will be announced, I am sure, with monthly rapidity. A good example of this is the way meats are available in so many lessened-fat forms, along with entire supermarket and health food departments for low-sodium, low-fat, low-cholesterol foods. Although the taste doesn't seem as "genuine" to me (is it psychological?), beef and pork are being bred and marketed in leaner, fat-freer products, too. Eating "right" is easier and easier.

Research and lab testing have also changed statistics on admissible cholesterol consumption. Shellfish, once considered too high in cholesterol, are now accepted because they are almost without saturated fat, are low in calories (if moderately consumed), and are nearly pure protein. Shrimp, lobster, and crab rate very low scores on the "cholesterol/saturated fat index"—one-third the score of ordinary ground beef. Oysters, scallops, and clams, while considered moderately high in cholesterol, are now believed to have enough redeeming qualities, that is, low calories, low saturated fat content, and beneficial fatty acids, that they are cleared for reasonably spaced "heart healthy" meals.

The Framingham Heart Study, well thought of among heart specialists, kept careful statistics for a number of years of residents of the Massachusetts town, checking cholesterol levels as they relate to the condition of hearts. Dr. William P. Castelli, the medical director of the study, speaking in 1988, made some strong assertions concerning cholesterol levels and coronary heart disease. He said cholesterol levels of 200–250 in a person can be dangerous, as *most* heart attacks occur at this level (whatever the underlying cause), even though such persons are usually not seen as high-risk patients. On the other, safety side, Dr. Castelli reported that during thirty-five years of the Framingham Heart Study, "I have not seen one case of coronary heart disease in anyone with a cholesterol level under 150 milligrams."

Among real sinner foods, few are as questionable as coconut oil and other coconut products used in so many processed food compounds (not to be confused with cocoa bean, as in chocolate). Coconut milk gets 82 percent of its calories from saturated fat (eleven teaspoons per cup), and coconut meat contains 76 percent saturated fat. Even a cup of dried, shredded meat contains five teaspoons. Since oats are a good source of the fiber that actually reduces LDL cholesterol, Dr. Castelli says, "I think what went wrong in America in the last fifty years is that we've gotten away from eating our oatmeal in the morning."

Most heart programs, including transplant programs, through diet, exercise, and medication, seek to lower cholesterol levels to under 200 and keep them there. Although a high cholesterol count is nearly always part of the problem (at least) with atherosclerosis, it is not always an accompaniment of cardiomyopathy. But it assumes great importance to every transplantee whose new heart represents "starting over" with respect to what might develop in the way of coronary disease. You may not have had a cholesterol problem with your old heart, but with this heart, things could turn out differently.

Almost as important for heart patients, before and after surgery, as cutting down your cholesterol count and keeping it down is increasing your aerobic exercise commitment. Aerobics is a fairly new addition to medical nomenclature, entering the vocabulary in the late 1960s through the auspices of Dr. Ken Cooper, who first designed what he named aerobic routines for the Air Force. Some years back he opened his now-famous Aerobics Center in Dallas, making it one of the most popular institutions in the world for care and testing of the heart. Dr. Cooper's aerobics program wasn't immediately seized upon with great affection by cardiologists. A good many of them were sincerely perturbed, predicting that an unacceptable percentage of those going through his vigorous aerobic exercise programs might keel over during some of the workouts and races his patients were often urged to get involved in. Within a few years, however, the word "aerobics" entered our dictionaries, and the idea of aerobic exercises that elevate your pulse rate and push up your oxygen consumption is accepted almost universally as being beneficial to heart patients, pre and post operations.

How is the nation doing now that every second page of the daily newspaper carries exercise information and warnings about avoiding heart problems? Great? Well, at the beginning of the 1980s, the Center for Disease Control, a government agency, published "Objectives for the Nation," a long-range report on eleven physical fitness goals for the next decade. By the end of that predicted period, the Center, in a later report, sadly concluded that at least five of the

eleven goals would not be met even though it was increasingly evident that regular physical activity reduced the occurrence of several
diseases and benefited the fight against heart disease, colon cancer,
diabetes, and obesity.

The Center had hoped that by 1990 the proportion of American
adults age eighteen to sixty-five who participated in the desirable
optimum of three times per week with twenty vigorous minutes of
exercise "should exceed 60 percent." Instead, only about 8 percent
of American adults exercise at such a level. Half of the Americans
over sixty-five, the Center's report had hoped, would walk, swim, or
engage in other appropriate aerobic exercise at least three times a
week. Again, expectations far exceeded performance. While 46 percent of these older Americans said they walked for exercise, only 8
percent actually met the three-times-a-week, twenty-minute goals.
And although children were more active than adults, the later report
found shocking statistics that produced equally sad response in proportion to activity among children as among the adults. Most persons
who have heart trouble have coronary atherosclerosis, and this is
what most exercise programs try to prevent or stabilize.

After discovering I had a heart problem, I used to dream aloud
from time to time: Wouldn't it be wonderful if tomorrow I got up
and through some miracle my heart was well again? And friends
offered all sorts of remedies, some of them apparently effective in
some cardiac circumstances. (I checked with my cardiologist before
trying anything, of course, and Dr. Kraus was reasonably permissive,
although warning me at intervals not to get my hopes too high.) One
charming friend was so full of advice about natural substances I
began calling her "Dr. She." Another friend, whose son is Dean
Ornish, a California medical doctor offering seminar-retreats in drug-
less cardiac improvement through diet and stress control, gave me
all sorts of reading matter having to do with the heart. Dr. Ornish,
who, beyond diet, puts great trust in meditation and relaxation
exercises, announced in 1988 the first measurable reversal of coronary atherosclerosis through his methods. He also said, "I think the
mind is where heart disease begins for many people."

Although their research findings were based on coronary disease more than on cardiomyopathy, some doctors have offered reasonable evidence that what they term "cynical attitudes and hostile emotions" of Type A (driven) behavior can excite biological responses leading to coronary disease. They contend that such driven, harried actions, by causing frequent large increases in the bodily chemicals that react to stress, can hurt coronary arteries, these injuries attracting cholesterol the way a magnet holds iron filings, thus blocking blood flow and bringing on heart attacks. Dr. Redford Williams, author of *The Trusting Heart: Great News About Type A Behavior,* offers numerous psychological steps away from cynicism and belligerence and toward what he terms "a trusting heart." Meyer Friedman and Ray Rosenman, the researchers who first described Type A behavior, cite "spiritual need" and "deep-seated anxiety" as underlying crises among the coronary prone. In his book, *The Relaxation Response,* cardiologist Herbert Benson suggests use of a repetitive prayer to produce "sharp reductions in heartbeat and blood pressure." This may seem like an unusual medical prescription for our day and time, but it's nothing new. Some readers may recall the directions given in the anonymous Russian classic *The Way of a Pilgrim* for unceasing interior prayer to soothe and refresh the Pilgrim: "Sit down alone and in silence. Lower your head, shut your eyes, breathe out gently and imagine yourself looking into your own heart. Carry your mind, *i.e.,* your thoughts, from your head to your heart. As you breathe out, say 'Lord Jesus Christ, have mercy on me.' Say it moving your lips gently, or simply say it in your mind. Try to put all other thoughts aside. Be calm, be patient, and repeat the process very frequently." Substituting whatever deity one wishes to approach, or no deity at all, this stress-reduction formula fits the needs of many endangered hearts.

Psychologist James Lynch's research finds high blood pressure, an important cardiac danger signal, often involves a communication problem. Blood pressure goes up when we talk, even if we're using sign language, he says, and goes down when we listen. Psychologist Larry Scherwitz, to combat some of the "I-me-my" self-centeredness that seems to lead to many heart attacks, advises, "Fall in love!"

One of the most challenging books on these lines is Robert Ornstein and David Sobel's *Healthy Pleasures.* This little volume takes up "medical terrorism," which keeps a patient (not necessarily a transplant patient) from enjoying life. Depriving ourselves of pleasure (or indulgences) such as eating ice cream can make us vulnerable to depression and physical fitness. Reach out and touch someone, literally, the authors urge; laugh more, see friends, get a hospital room with a view, and you'll recover quicker than sweating out life in some closed cubicle. Then, at home, take up gardening, buy a dog or a cat, and watch a sunset.

Several veterans of the Pritikin spartan diet-exercise routine suggested I try that program. But the problem with so much of this good advice was that it didn't apply to cardiomyopathy. Products or procedures that worked for victims of heart disease simply couldn't be applied to cases of heart failure. My heart was dying, and I came to accept this unenviable condition.

Betty's sister Mary Lillian Darden gave me a copy of Norman Cousins' book, *Anatomy of an Illness,* which tells how Mr. Cousins' mind (with the help of megadoses of vitamin C) apparently cured his body of a quite debilitating tissue disease. Although I have always leaned toward the idea of mind over matter, I could not find myself in Mr. Cousins' holistic medical picture. He does make exceptional points, however, which I think everyone, sick or well, must consider. "I was greatly elated by the discovery that there is a physiologic basis for the ancient theory that laughter is a good medicine," he wrote, and in a later interview, after working for a decade on the faculty of the University of California at Los Angeles School of Medicine, he stated, "There's now a scientific basis for believing that hope, faith, love, and the will to live have a bearing on the outcome of an illness."

I have always thought laughter a wonderful medicine in itself, inspired from boyhood when *Reader's Digest* began its famous "Laughter Is the Best Medicine" department. Some readers are going to ask, How can you talk about laughter when someone faces death? I answer, What better time to talk about laughter? In the prime of life, laughter comes easily, comes naturally, and can seldom be suppressed. It is an accompanying condition to all the good things we list, the most precious moments, the sacred times of acknowledging that life is a worthwhile experience. And if happiness and laughter are two sides of the same coin, then what more effective time to laugh than when that life becomes endangered and existence is in the dice?

I am convinced there are no limits to what the mind can do. There are undoubted limits to my mind's performance, but my limits may not be true of others. There may be medical coincidences (juxtapositions?) along *with* this conviction, but I believe its efficacy, its potential for cure, is *there* in virtually any kind of illness. In my case, determination seemed to support the failing animal, although my physicians may disagree or think I'm ungrateful if I put too much emphasis on determination alone in contrast to their skills. I don't preach to convert on the topic, no matter what my feelings are.

I certainly believe that stress can injure the body and that "good thoughts" (whatever your definition of "good thoughts") can provide emotional levels which make avoidance of stress easier and treatment more effective. I also believe the impact of your environment can create physical and emotional predicaments beyond ordinary depression. Dallas psychiatrist Salomon Grimberg, who worked for years among Mexican artist Frida Kahlo's mysterious paintings of blood and death, said, "They are charged with a negative energy that can destroy. People who are very involved with the work of Frida Kahlo are contaminated by this energy. That's why I'm through with her. I could live with her paintings forever, but they suck you dry."

I've been a longtime believer in psychosomatic medicine (symptoms caused or eased by the relationship between the mind and the body). The effect of the mind on healing—psychological persuasion and the use of placebo pills with control groups, that sort of thing—is well documented. The religious aspects of healing are strongly believed in by thousands, although I'm not sure how many, if any, medical practitioners in general believe so strongly. Persons near terminal cases often say there are no atheists in hospital beds, just as in World War II it was said there were no atheists in foxholes; it's very difficult to lie in bed with a terrible disease or terrible pain and not seek some kind of a third-person appeal for relief. Something to believe in, something to hold on to—whether it is yourself, God, the medical advances of today, fate, your doctor—there must be a substance outside the ordinary possibilities of the coin toss.

But don't think for a moment no panic is involved when the news first overwhelms you that the red flag is up, the warning lights are beginning to blink, there's ice on the highway, and the sand and salt crews are somewhere down at the other end of the county. It is a bewildering experience to feel your heart dying spiritually as well as literally.

So like most heart patients, when I learned I not only had heart trouble but of a rather mysterious but progressively deadly sort, I could not escape a feeling of despair, regardless of assurances, optimistic predictions, and offered evidence. For some heart victims despair eventually lessens, but there are few heroic moments in heart trouble, especially if you are facing a dangerous and highly conjectural future, the heart inside you ticking down, down, down to doom, doom, doom.

My dying heart's deterioration wasn't something I could reverse by will alone. There was possibly a time when willpower might have overpowered decay or when someone of firmer convictions than mine could perform what appeared to be superhuman recoveries or corrections. But my heart muscle was stretched too far, like a rubber band left overlong in sunlight and heat. There was no resilience, nothing physiologic for hope, faith, love, and laughter to build on.

I had to live with both the knowledge and the real dimensions of that knowledge.

Chapter 5

The degeneration of my heart was gradual, decline coming day by day, week by week, month by month, but I quickly started recognizing there were things I had been capable of doing a few days or weeks ago that I had imperceptibly lost the ability to do. It was frustrating, inconvenient, and embarrassing. I gladly gave up some of the sweaty things, such as operating a lawn mower and fixing shingles on the roof, and by the end of that hot summer I also gave up the idea of doing the brisk laps in the swimming pool I had promised myself I would do, sticking instead to sitting neck-deep in the water or merely dog-paddling. But I also had to give up some little everyday things a man, especially a householder, thinks nothing of until he's unable to do them or has to have help to finish them. For one, I discovered I couldn't twist open those devilishly difficult jar lids on command ("Here, honey, open these olives for me") or bring in enough firewood in one load for half a winter's day.

I would not tell anyone how much I imagined things inside my chest were dwindling and weakening, but within a few months of Bill Kraus's grim pronouncement I had made myself quit standing on ladders, step stools, or chair seats to reach things off high shelves, and I started watching carefully as I went down steps in case a series of irregular heartbeats caused me to spin out. (It never happened, I'm glad to say.) The strength of my medication was increased and the PVCs were kept controlled, but my heart was still dying. Then accepting the seriousness of it, I entered stage three: the dying heart making itself owner and controller of my life.

During this "don't admit nuthin'!" period, which lasted for several months, I tried to shield my family and friends—and myself—from the alarms that occasionally struck me. I didn't deny my condition, but I masked it. If someone asked, "How are you doing?" my reply was an overly sincere smile and, "Great!" If the questioner was too close to me to accept an obviously false response, I would smile wanly and say, "Good" or a temporizing "Okay."

This guarded optimism (or self-deception or, if you want to call it that, lying!) helped me because, if nothing else, the mask of sufficiency seemed to compensate for the loss of control. I do know that during my frequent visits to the lab and the examination room, my blithe outward attitude tried to deny my worsening inward reactions. I found myself asking, with every determination, will it hurt my heart? My imagination worked overtime, as the imagination tends to do in periods of medical stress. Every little pain or sudden twitch must be overcome mentally. Even knowing that by medical standards I was unlikely to have angina pains or a coronary "attack," I still went through quick spasms of doubt. Was that a real heart pain or was it indigestion? Is my heart about to fibrillate, or is this pounding merely from climbing the stairs too fast? Without meaning to sound stoic—for I certainly wasn't—I pledged to myself that I would not let my days become a series of ups and downs on a mental or emotional roller-coaster. I lectured myself about taking the down days at the same level as the good ones, even if "good" was more comparative than concrete. (Scared? Of course I was. Looking back, I tell myself I was brave, steadfast, calm, and wise. What folly! I have my daily journals to confront such hindsight recollecting.)

But relief can also be found in mental persuasions. For example, I was doing quite a bit of flying, and I became convinced that once the plane got to cabin pressure height my heart felt and worked better. I would land at my destination much energized by my flight. When I mentioned this to Bill Kraus, however, he smiled (that obliging way medical professionals have) and without being unkind assured me it was mostly psychological.

Psychological? My entire existence became psychological, from my point of view. Despite its insidious nature, the image of the incurably dying heart is never very far from the realization of the one who holds the heart within him. What had been the most dependable organ becomes treacherous, a time bomb in the chest, a dagger in the mind. Being a man who worked with words and ideas, everything I started reading, writing, or reviewing eventually turned me to one end: the heart. And the way you suddenly encounter a word everywhere once you see it for the first time, every literary reference to the heart suddenly became doleful. It inflicted my work. I found myself drifting into sentimentality to the point of becoming maudlin when I let my feelings go. "But oh, heart, heart, it is you who must be obeyed" were the first lines of a poem I tried to pour my heart out with, but (thank God) never finished, couldn't finish.

Everywhere I turned there were reminders of that mortality. Even my favorite poet, William Butler Yeats, speaks of "the foul rag-and-bone shop of the heart" and penned lines I feared might be prophetic:

> *Consume my heart away; sick with desire*
> *And fastened to a dying animal*
> *It knows not what it is . . .*

Thoughts like these, as inevitable as they are transitory, afflict those who undergo the frustration of not being able to do something beneficial to their condition. It is the worst kind of captivity—the captivity of your mind within the captivity of your body, parts of which may be free, which makes it that much worse. There was no medical remedy I could attempt, no exercise, no regimen, no changed daily routine that would avail me of relief, so all the alleviation I had was mental. Although I tried never to make comparisons between myself and victims of terminal diseases, I came to understand why many of them eventually accepted the most outrageous scams and frauds in the way of "cures" simply because there was nothing else they could do—and it does little good to tell a dying spirit that its hope is false.

Why me? That's the question I think every heart problem raises. A few persons, perhaps too starkly honest for their own good, may give themselves answers, reasons such as, "I earned it." In my case, having observed the rules, I felt I was being unjustly penalized when I discovered that I had heart trouble. I whined a bit and played living with a touch of fraudulence, but I didn't quit life. Not yet. Even when my condition became unquestionably enfeebling I continued to do as many as I could of the things I had done before. I continued with my literary work, continued making a few speaking engagements, kept on working around the house, continued driving an automobile, taking trips. In fact, there was an eighteen-month period after the desperate diagnosis when I did more editing work, with its long, slow, and laborious hours, than I had done since my daily newspaper days back in the 1960s. But there was no denying the constant depletion of energy, the loss of exhilaration, the lack of "feeling good." Also, I was seeing my cardiologist more frequently, treading water, more or less, with medications that proved effective for a while, then lost their power. Some days I would wake convinced—for a while, at least—that something had happened to make me feel stronger, that once again I was on a pathway toward some sort of recovery, some means of making up a bit of the lost ground. It was hope, undying, persistent, and foolish, but inspirational. I deliberately refused to inspect it closely; I didn't want to go overboard forward or aft, but I wanted to hold on to that hope. And the major asset I brought out of that time was the recognition of the place of hope in every phase of human life. I'll nag on the point, and I'll add this seemingly ridiculous tenet: Don't inspect hope too closely. Seize on hope, but don't try to define it. There is no such thing as inspected hope. The very nature of the thing denies the term.

The first summer after I joined the faculty of the University of North Texas in Denton (about thirty miles north of my home in Dallas), my assigned office was located on the third floor of a tall building, and before the first semester was over my heart's capability had descended to the point where I had to pause and gulp a few breaths before being able to make it up the final flight of stairs. Of course I didn't want to admit I was that weak, and I tried to cover my weakness with all kinds of elaborate, even theatrical, gestures and posings so I could pause and rest: stopping on the stairs to pretend

I was illustrating a joke to some invisible companion, dropping my briefcase (in one hilarious episode that proved disastrous to the briefcase), pretending to wave at or halting to address someone on the landing above or below—who wasn't there. Dr. James Ward Lee, who assumed the chair of the English department a short time later, saw to it that as soon as possible I was given an office in a building with an operating elevator, which saved my academic career if not my life. Jim's father had died of congestive heart failure, so he knew something about what I was going through.

In May 1987, Betty and I went with Tom and Taina Dozier, Betty's brother and his wife, to spend a few days between terms at their mountain home above Ruidosa, New Mexico. I knew it was a mistake almost from the moment I stepped out of the car when we arrived there. The scenery was breathtaking, but that wasn't what was taking my breath away. The altitude (above nine thousand feet) hit me terribly. That night I scared everybody so badly with my labored breathing (I could be heard all over the three-bedroom home) and my inability to sleep lying down in a bed that Tom and Taina wanted us to turn around and return to Dallas posthaste. Wheezing and panting I protested "it was nothing," but another night of my snorting and bellowing as I tried to sleep in a chair and they brushed aside my feeble protests of "No, really, I feel okay," and we returned to Dallas where I was absolutely pooped but at least able to get a few hours' sleep.

Then in July and August I suffered a continuing series of sleepless nights and listless days, with virtually no appetite. At one point I wrote of myself, "I'm having cold sweats. I feel terrible, too; heaving, panting, etc." Then: "I break down *so* quickly. . . . Staying in bed I'm so weak. . . . Another 'Bed Sunday,' didn't even read the papers." Betty's journal is full of such entries as: "A.C. had a terrible night— practically no sleep. Bill [Kraus] has just *got* to find a better formula for his medicine. A.C. is getting very little rest or serenity." In August I whined: "I just don't feel very much like I'll live long."

Finally, on August 10, I surrendered to the reality of my situation. I called Bill Kraus and admitted I was not doing nearly so well as I had been pretending. He had me do the laboratory/X ray/EKG routine, and on August 12 we had a good news–bad news conference. The good news was, he said, a new medicine, Enkaid, for which he had high expectations. He hoped it would control my arrhythmia without depressing the heart muscle. I was the first patient he'd put on Enkaid. The bad news was that it had to work: Mine was the sort of heart problem a pacemaker couldn't be used for, and he felt I was too old for a transplant. It was drugs or nothing. Betty wrote, "I just hope we can find the right one, pray God."

The medication didn't work, or at least it didn't work the way we had hoped. On September 1, Bill called Betty and they had a telephone consultation—I only found out about it later, from her journal. Bill admitted to her just how bad my heart muscle was and said that I must begin to think about a transplant, as slender as that hope might be. He said he would tell me but wanted to prepare her. Betty hesitated to ask that overwhelming question, but Bill answered it for her: "Without it he *may* have a year." She wrote, "I feel as though I've been hit with a club."

Next day Betty and I went to the hospital to see Bill, and I wrote of the occasion: "He's not too sanguine—thinks I'm worse off than I do." He said he was stepping up and strengthening my medication, but he expected good results. As I recall, a transplant was mentioned, but I was so convinced it was both too dangerous and out of the question that I failed to read the urgency Bill was trying to put across. Betty wrote, "A.C. seems not to be considering a transplant but *I* am."

Chapter 6

A day of inevitable disability was reached, a day when even hopeless hope had to be suspended. No more pretense of recovery, no more gestures and attempts to cover up what was so obviously a panting, desperate cripple. One day after the usual lab tests, X rays, and EKG (stress testing had long been given up), Bill Kraus sat me down and made me face certain certainties: My heart was drawing nearer its inevitable death, and its death would be my death. What is the answer? I asked, knowing what he had to say. There is an answer, Bill said, a heart transplant—if it can still be done, based on the condition your other organs may have gotten in from your bad heart, if you can be accepted by some transplant program, and if a donor heart can be found once you are admitted to a program.

It was not a happy prognosis, he warned me; I might be too old for a transplant program to accept me, I might not be in as good general shape as I should be, and even if accepted by a program, I had to wait, and waiting for a new heart could stretch into desperate weeks. In addition, the operation was long and hard, and even with health insurance, the costs were bound to be enormous; the loss of time alone could run into thousands of dollars, especially for someone like me who earned most of his living through his daily output. And there was no guarantee that I would survive the transplant operation under the best of prospects. A dozen or a hundred things could happen, more of them bad than good. It's *win* or *lose;* heart transplant is not a game that can end in a tie. Was I prepared? Did I have the *heart* for it?

There was no alternative except unconditional surrender; arguments in favor of or against a transplant become empty rhetoric when death is the inevitable conclusion. I took little time to ponder the question. My heart told me to do it, and once I made that decision and told Bill it was made unhesitatingly, he began supporting my decision by describing the potentiality of a new heart. His positive response helped me turn a corner of calmness, giving me the renewal of hope that I had almost lost. Faint and frail it might have been, but it was firm enough for me to build around it, to turn hope into faith, with a measure of medical assurance mixed in to make it more concrete. I firmly believe the attitude of the physician is vital to the health of the patient. For myself, I was not able to enter and pass through the valley of shadow on the strength alone of a stalwart spirit—though there may be millions who can. I needed some spiritual armature around which to construct emotional firmness, even if I had to use clay for its ultimate shape. Never again did Bill Kraus and I let gloom or the possibility of doom taint our doctor-patient relationship.

Early in September I began teaching again, although Bill didn't think I should. On September 9 I filmed a "MacNeil/Lehrer News Hour" television segment with producer Mike Saltz. It was filmed outdoors, and Mike later told me he almost kept it off the air, I was so sick and worn out. Meredith said I looked like a ghost. She and Jim Lee were along on the shoot, and watching me, they agreed privately I was a fool to have done it. I wouldn't have admitted it, but I had to agree with them.

On September 21 Bill Kraus and I met with another cardiologist friend, Dr. Jack Hyland, at Baylor Medical Center, and I was interviewed by two transplant specialists. Neither Bill nor Jack had much to say as I left Baylor. I realized the conference had not been hopeful, and in fact, a few days later I was told I would not be accepted in Baylor's program as a transplant recipient. But I knew a heart transplant was my only hope of surviving beyond a few more months. By

September 25, after conferring with the personnel officer at the university and finding what coverage my insurance offered, I told Bill to go ahead with whatever transplant plans might be possible, and he told me not to give up despite the fact that I had been turned down by the one program.

The story of human transplantation is young, as history goes, but medically it is into its second or third generation. Successful kidney transplants were begun in the 1950s, generally using a kidney from a close kin. Humans can usually get along very well on one kidney, so it is possible to use living donors, and such is generally the case. Within a few years after the first successful kidney transplants, recipients were pursuing ordinary lives, and in the case of some of the women, having children.

Successful heart transplantation had a dramatic introduction on December 3, 1967, when Dr. Christiaan N. Barnard and two surgical teams of Groote Shuur Hospital in Cape Town, South Africa, replaced the badly diseased heart of Louis Washkansky, a fifty-five-year-old grocer, with the heart from Denise Ann Darvall, a twenty-five-year-old bank employee who had died in an automobile accident. (And what most people have forgotten or didn't hear, Miss Darvall's kidneys were also transplanted successfully into ten-year-old Jonathan Van Wyk.)

Louis Washkansky had suffered from diabetes and heart disease; he had suffered a massive heart attack that severely crippled the left ventricle, making it swell like a balloon; two coronary arteries were clogged; and he was confined to the hospital. But the doctors later said his spirit was so good that despite his condition (he would probably not be offered a heart today) he was considered suitable for the experiment, and when offered the chance for a transplant, knowing it was a gamble almost past useful odds, he unhesitatingly accepted.

Following the operation, Washkansky joked about it, calling himself a Frankenstein monster because of the stranger's heart he now had. Washkansky lived only eighteen days, dying of pneumonia. The immunosuppressant drugs given to prevent rejection of the transplanted organ heightened the risk of infection, as was so often to be the case with early transplants, making him easy prey for the germs and bacteria that pose little or no danger in the normal, healthy person.

Still, the entire world was magnetized by the "Miracle at Cape Town," and forty-five-year-old Christiaan Barnard, a handsome, telegenic figure, gained overnight fame. A month later, using the team of surgeons, technicians, and nurses he had assembled, he transplanted a heart into Philip Blaiberg, who ultimately lived seventeen months, and that not only made the medical world admit the procedure could be successful but started a wave of such operations worldwide. Dr. Barnard became a jet-set celebrity, remarried a beautiful younger woman, and was the toast of the media world. But the jet-set image galled many doctors; one of them stated it pretty much for the rest when he called Barnard's media blitz "in poor taste." (Although a lot of the criticism of Dr. Barnard was unfair, he did not seem averse to the publicity, becoming an international figure who was pictured with heads of state and entertainment personalities, which physicians were unaccustomed to.)

There was a general feeling that Barnard hadn't given his American counterparts enough credit and had pulled a publicity stunt by rushing into a human heart transplant before the operation had been "cleared" by some of the persons who had brought it to the point where Barnard could succeed with it. Barnard had studied in the United States in the mid-1950s at the University of Minnesota, where Dr. Norman Shumway had a surgery fellowship, and studied cardiology with Dr. John Kirklin at the Mayo Clinic in Minnesota. He had visited Dr. Shumway and Dr. Richard Lower at Stanford (where Shumway had been performing successful heart transplants on dogs) earlier in 1967.

Some surgeons criticized the rush to do heart transplants as "an international race to be a member of the 'me-too' brigade" and warned the operation was far from being a safe or needed procedure. Barnard and others pointed out that without a transplant the patient was doomed. Within a year many of the critics were doing heart transplants in their own clinics. Dr. Denton Cooley (under whom Barnard had once worked), who had opposed the idea earlier, saying that heart transplantation needed more study, quickly became the prime heart transplant surgeon in the United States, basing his sudden change of heart on advances in surgical techniques. Within eight months of Barnard's first transplant, Cooley had done ten at his Texas Heart Institute in Houston, more than any other surgeon.

That first wave of heart transplants soon petered out. Three years after the Cape Town Miracle only a handful of heart transplant patients were still alive across the globe. All of Cooley's patients were dead. The problem was not surgical but medical: The immunosuppressant given to prevent rejection of the transplanted organ seemingly couldn't be controlled. Patients died from the infections and diseases allowed into the body after the destruction of the immune system. To be sure, not every heart transplantee was doomed, even from those earliest days. Emmanuel Vitria of Marseilles, France, who died in May 1987 at age sixty-seven, had had his transplanted heart for eighteen and a half years, a new record for survival time. And by December of that year, Willem Van Buuren, an American citizen who had received a new heart at age forty under Dr. Shumway's Stanford University program, was celebrating his "nearly uneventful course" after almost eighteen years, and two years later was still alive. However, as Barnard said of his patient Blaiberg's lengthy (for the time) survival, these are possibly aberrations, perhaps resulting from some unusual composition in the patient's physical makeup—except in the case of Van Buuren, whose survival seems a tribute to the Stanford transplant program. Although Emmanuel Vitria survived for a record number of years, he was never able to return to work.

Another major problem in early heart transplantation was the lack of any way to detect a rejection event quickly. The earlier that rejection is recognized and treated, the more effective suppressant drug therapy becomes. Many deaths occurred because intervention therapy was applied too late; in other words, the body's tightrope walk between the immune system and the medication became unbalanced before equilibrium could be restored, and the "performer" fell. The only means for discovering rejection were use of the EKG, studying blood pressure, and listening to heart sounds. But the heart was usually in an extreme condition before these methods alerted the medical professionals. Even X ray couldn't disclose the necessary information about encroaching immune cells. Something was needed that would enable the laboratory literally to study a portion of tissue for such evidence.

In the face of the grim survival statistics, most heart transplant surgeons, including Cooley, quit the practice. Dr. Barnard still did heart transplants and later came to the United States to set up a transplantation program in Oklahoma. After a fairly short time, however, he had to retire from active surgery due to crippling arthritis in his hands, and in 1988 he returned to South Africa. Only Shumway continued through the 1970s to do cardiac transplants, giving a new chance at life to nearly 50 percent of his patients.

Then in 1973 Philip Caves, a Scottish surgeon working under Shumway at Stanford, solved the problem of rejection detection when he developed the endomyocardial (heart) biopsy. This procedure, now done with such regularity as to be almost casual, sends a catheter (tube) from an opening in the neck through a vein to the heart where a pincer-equipped cable, or bioptome, threaded through the tube pinches off tiny pieces of heart—less than the size of a lead pencil point. These pieces are brought back out the same vein for lab study. This sounds rather daunting, but the reality of it is not quite as painful as the description. Although done under operating room conditions, only a surface anesthetic is generally needed, and there is little or no pain once the catheter enters the vein. In fact, after the first two or three biopsies, the heart transplantee can watch the monitor screen and see the bioptome at work in his heart, feeling nothing. (As I write this I hold in my hand the bioptome apparatus. Since such instruments are used only once, Dr. Kraus and the cath lab crew, on finishing a particularly stringent biopsy, presented it to me as a reward for good behavior.)

Despite the introduction of the heart biopsy, the body's immune system—the guardian against infection that overdoes it with transplants—seemed to reject a "foreign" heart severely, and rejection events for any type of transplant could, and often did, strike months or years after transplantation; in addition, the heart as an organ doesn't have the ischemic time (how long an organ can be preserved without a blood supply) that an organ such as the liver has. This means that while a liver transplant operation is usually longer and can be more dangerous because of the number and locations of blood vessels and ducts attached to the liver, there is a little more lead time in procuring the organ, getting it into the recipient, and getting it to function. The heart not only survives for a shorter time but has to start working, and working well, almost instantaneously once in place. (Increasingly effective preservative compounds used on donor livers and kidneys have not proven as useful with hearts. The heart, being a muscle, not a spongelike gland such as the liver and the kidneys, must have protein "fuel" to keep it alive. It is a motor, both a pump and a receptor.)

Advances in drugs and their use continued, even as the transplants failed. Dr. Thomas Starzl, later renowned as head of the transplant work at the University of Pittsburgh (the busiest such center in the United States), by 1973 had developed what was known as "cocktail therapy" which combined two drugs for better rejection control after kidney transplantation, and subsequently added antilymphocyte globulin (ALG) to make a three-drug "cocktail."

Reports of drug side effects, particularly the steroid prednisone, from earlier days of heart transplantation remain scary. The late Tommy Thompson, in his 1971 bestseller *Hearts,* described what were then typical reactions to steroids in the Houston transplant program: "Many became depressed, and for brief periods, psychotic. Some had total withdrawal, lying mute, catatonic in their beds . . . others burst into tears for no apparent reason. Some could not sleep, others *would* not sleep." Thompson told of transplantees whose faces swelled up "like balloons" but added that even this didn't begin to accurately describe "the distortion and disfigurement that could be caused by steroids." One Texas transplantee, he said, suffered the horror of having his face "chewed away by herpes virus. His body resistance was so lowered by the immunosuppressive drugs that the disease ran rampant. . . . [He] had been a splendid-looking man but could no longer even bear to look at himself in the mirror." He did not survive. These were some of the reasons my cardiologist, even after he knew what was wrong with my heart, had not wanted to offer transplantation as the immediate solution.

But in November 1983 a drug was introduced that has more than lived up to the designation "miracle drug." It was cyclosporine, and

the romantic story of its discovery and development is worth telling
in detail. The famous Swiss drug house Sandoz Chemical Company
makes a practice of requiring its scientists to bring back soil samples
from whatever part of the world they visit—even on vacation. In
1970 one such scientist, Jean-François Borel, vacationing in Norway,
dug up and sacked a few ounces of tundra soil in a bleak upland
region called Hardangervidda. (Writer Lee Gutkind, in his book
Many Sleepless Nights, describes it almost poetically as "this vast
and untouched primeval landscape, carpeted with mosses, lichens,
and treeless grasslands, dotted with crystal blue lakes, rolling hills,
and gigantic glacial boulders.") An analysis of the soil gathered on
this isolated plateau (that's what *vidda* means in Norwegian) showed
it contained a unique amino acid named tolypocladium inflastum
gans, or TIG. Researchers thought it might be used as an antifungal
agent or an antibiotic, and no thought was given to its use as an
immunosuppressant. Although TIG worked against some blights, it
didn't seem to have commercial possibilities—which a drug laboratory looks for, to be sure—and it was given a number and filed away.

Later, Borel, a thirty-five-year-old Swiss-French biologist (once a
student at the University of Wisconsin), carried on experiments with
certain extractions of TIG and discovered the compound suppressed
the immune systems of laboratory mice but did not kill other cells.
Further experiments proved the compound could suppress a large
spectrum of immune reactions without destroying the immune system itself. The compound, first named "ciclosporin," was shortly
renamed "cyclosporine." A paper presenting its unusual properties
was read to a British medical society, and a British scientist reported
what he had heard to his colleague, Roy Calne, who helped develop
the use of azathioprine in the 1960s and was the major transplant
surgeon in Great Britain (knighted for his work in 1981, he died in
1987). A few precious milligrams of ciclosporin were made available
to Calne, and his experiments on animal hearts so dramatically
increased survival rates that he enthusiastically contacted Sandoz for
more of the substance. The drug company replied that it had been
dropped from research and there was no more.

Calne visited the Sandoz plant in Basel and persuaded the management (who were very "bottom-line," as American businessmen

might put it) to start production of cyclosporine, predicting that organ transplants were the biggest thing in the medical future. A decade later, cyclosporine had become Sandoz's largest-selling drug in the United States. However, early human experiments weren't all promising. In fact, even Calne was forced to admit that use of the drug caused a too-high cancer rate. Borel said that came very close to being the end for cyclosporine.

Experimentation in the United States continued, and it was found that cyclosporine, to be safer, must be combined with steroids and the dosages cut drastically. In addition, a new form of the drug, Cyclosporine A, was developed and proved more effective and less lethal than the first compound. However, it still lacked a dependable vehicle to get it to metabolize in the human system. It happened that one of the English lab scientists working on the problem of metabolization was Greek and usually ate at a nearby Greek restaurant. It occured to him that olive oil might be a better suspension agent than water or alcohol had been. He obtained a liter of Greek olive oil from the restaurant, which imported it in barrels, used the oil as a vehicle for the dosing of cyclosporine, and as has been said before, the rest is history. (I think of this man when I do my twice-a-day dose of cyclosporine and use hot water to wash out my glass—cyclosporine clouds plastic. I smell the resinlike fragrance of, presumably, Greek olive oil.) Today, cyclosporine is produced in Austria in tanks fifty feet high.

So dramatic was cyclosporine's effectiveness that the U. S. Food and Drug Administration, which ordinarily enforces years of human testing before a new drug is allowed on the United States market, made cyclosporine available a short period following its proven value in transplants. The transplant industry in the United States boomed after November 1983 when the FDA finally approved cyclosporine for general medical use. By 1985 heart transplantation was being done at more and more medical and surgical centers. The survival rate rose steadily until, by the time I recognized that I had to have a new heart, the odds were nearer 70–30 in my favor than the 49–51 odds in favor of fate of only a few years before. Cyclosporine also hastened the effectiveness of liver transplantation so that, combined with surgical experience, by the mid-1980s that operation was being successfully performed on a near-routine basis at some centers. (Pancreas transplant has not been nearly as extensive or as successful as other kinds of transplantation, with a one-year survival rate of under 33 percent.)

Despite its great success as a survival tool, the use of cyclosporine is not without predicament: It can cause kidney problems in as many as one-third of its users and high blood pressure in about 25 percent of all transplantees. And since the rate of rejection is slowed so dramatically by cyclosporine, it becomes harder to diagnose or predict rejection events; therefore, biopsies have to be done more frequently. Still, there is no question of cyclosporine's value and virtue, and undoubtedly substitutes will be made as well as advances in drugs themselves. In fact, experimentation continues with more powerful immunosuppressant drugs. A Japanese-produced experimental immunosuppressant (bearing a number) was a thousand times more potent than cyclosporine, but its very power made it too lethal for continued human use. However, in 1989 a dramatic series of experiments was successfully concluded that proved the drug (called FK 506) to be much more useful and less dangerous than cyclosporine, and the transplant world waited anxiously for its general introduction and use.

Another development in heart transplantation was the artificial heart. Barney Clark, a fifty-four-year-old Seattle dentist, became the first human with a permanently implanted artificial heart (the famous Jarvik-7), and he lived nearly four months afterward; but following his death, his family said that the way he was forced to survive made the experiment "not worth it." Late in 1984 William Schroeder of Indiana lived over twenty months, a record for living with an artificial heart. At first his new heart was made a national emblem, with television following his progress and even showing the Jarvik-7–implanted Schroeder drinking his first can of beer. That was less than a month after the operation. By the second month he was the victim of a stroke that severely limited his speech and memory, and he required constant nursing care. Schroeder's and Clark's surgeon, Dr. William C. DeVries, made the following statement at Schroeder's funeral: "He pushed the seeds of a tree into the ground, knowing he might never live in its shade."

The Jarvik-7 tree, if you will, had still not succeeded in offering shelter for cardiac victims even several years later. Three other artificial heart patients also died after Barney Clark and William Schroeder, and no further implants were made. Early in 1990 the F.D.A. withdrew approval of continued experimental use of the Jarvik heart, citing deficiencies found in its manufacture. In May 1988 the National Institute of Health had ceased to finance research on artificial hearts. In a procedure in limited practice, Dr. Jack Copeland at the University of Arizona first used a mechanical heart as a "bridge" to sustain the patient until a donor heart could be found.

Experimentation along the transplant frontier continues and undoubtedly will continue as long as we humans must rely on that potentially flawed but reparable mechanism, the human heart. Questions about survival and reconstruction of reconstructed hearts can be answered better and clearer each year. For instance, can a second heart transplant be done on one person? Second organ transplants, including hearts, can and are done. Often the recipient of a second heart is a young person whose initial transplanted heart functioned poorly, though this is not always the case. A number of successful second transplants have been done after the passage of years, five at least. At this point age is a determining factor in such retransplanting, but that will probably change. Does this mean that someone may continue to receive hearts over and over until some other form of termination ends the aging process? Not yet, but who knows what the transplant future holds?

Medical advancement isn't the only heart "frontier." The heart is a rather strong muscle, and the medical world is no longer in awe of the human heart or afraid of bruising what was once considered almost too fragile to touch. Another 1989 news story told how an Illinois physician saved a gunshot victim from bleeding to death by plugging bullet holes in his heart with her fingers and massaging the organ during a fourteen-minute helicopter ride. Another surgeon, who called the action "unprecedented and heroic," said it was not unusual for a trauma surgeon to use fingers to block holes in the heart but that it's ordinarily done in the emergency room "only until you can get the patient to the operating room."

In the future more and more organ transplants will be done around the world. More and more surgeons will adopt the emerging transplant field as their specialty. Transplant surgery could rank with the greatest advancement in medical science. As Dr. Keith Reemtsma, chief surgeon at Columbia-Presbyterian Medical Center, was quoted by *The New York Times:* "Surgeons in the twenty-first century will spend most of their time replacing parts rather than removing them, as they have in the last century."

There is also the feeling among some transplant authorities, however, that heart replacement is about as successful as it is going to get until an artificial heart and power mechanism (nuclear?) are perfected. Others disagree, not about the procedure but about the product. Many cardiac surgeons feel that hearts of another species will be more successful than the inorganic substitutes of artificial devices. (There is already a word for transplanting from species to species—animal to human, for example—*xenography.*) Perhaps it is of interest to know that while a great deal of emotion has been displayed by persons who claim to respect animal rights, especially when animals are used in laboratory experiments, a more ordinary factor is having more effect on animal use in experimentation: economy. Certain animals that more closely conform to human anatomy and physiology are not only endangered but have become almost out of reach in price. A chimpanzee, for example, once used extensively in heart experimentation, if available would cost something like $10,000, and a baboon, not so scarce or endangered, still costs in excess of $1,200.

The survival rate for heart transplantation will soon reach the levels of the more traditional forms of major surgery, and there is little question but that new medicinal developments such as FK 506 will make survival easier if no more predictable. The only barrier to increased transplant operations of all kinds is the number of donor organs available.

Another medical frontier that many doctors (including Dr. Steves Ring, my transplant surgeon) think eventually will surpass transplantation in drama and importance is genetic engineering. Already creating amazement (and havoc) in the laboratory, it could solve many of the difficulties and even the impossibilities that face not only transplantation but other medical procedures and processes.

• • •

The center of transplantation experimentation and development in the United States has been generally credited to the University of Pittsburgh. Well before my own operation, I (along with most Dallas residents) had followed the Pittsburgh program with great attention because in February 1984 the world's first successful heart-liver transplant was done there by Dr. Thomas Starzl on six-year-old Stormie Jones of Texas. Stormie had to return to Pittsburgh with liver complications in 1988, and in 1990 had a second liver transplant done there. Her transplanted heart remained "strong and stable" according to Dr. Andreas Tzakis, who performed the second liver transplant. Unfortunately, another Dallas girl, seventeen-year-old Mary Cheatam, failed to survive a heart-liver transplant at Pittsburgh, not long after Stormie's earlier triumph.

Early in 1989 a research team from the University of Pittsburgh announced its use of a new preservative that proved to give donor livers three times the ischemic time formerly thought safe. It is a chilled mixture called UW-lactobionate; it can preserve human livers outside the body for twenty-four hours, where the time limit was formerly nine or so hours. A University of Wisconsin biochemist who helped develop the preservative, initially unveiled in 1987, reported it extended the ischemic time for the pancreas from six hours to more than twenty-four and had proven as effective for donor kidneys as the method being used, and was capable of preserving the kidneys for thirty to forty hours. At the time of the announcement the preservative solution had not been tried on human hearts but had extended the ischemic time for dog hearts to twelve hours. What this means is that all kinds of organ transplants will increase since transplant and procurement teams will have much greater headway in seeking and procuring organs as well as performing the operation itself.

Less than a week after the announcement of a new preservative, Dr. Starzl revealed that within an eight-month period, eleven cancer patients in Presbyterian-University Hospital who were thought to be terminally ill had undergone abdominal transplant surgery that replaced four of their cancerous or endangered abdominal organs with healthy organs. The group had involved ten men and three women, but two died, one after a second transplant. Surgical teams removed each patient's liver, pancreas, most or all of the stomach, two-thirds of the colon, and the duodenum. These were replaced by a new liver, pancreas, duodenum, and jejunum (part of the small intestine) from the same donor. What was attempted was the removal of the entire tumor plus all areas where it might have spread. Some of the original cancer-transplant patients were left without stomachs, but it has been pointed out that the stomach is not essential for digestion, which can be performed by the intestines. These stomachless patients must eat six small meals a day, spaced only an hour or two apart.

All thirteen of this initial group were near death and their tumors were inoperable, Starzl told the media. He said that all but the most recent survivors, including one who had undergone the operation only five days before, had gone home. Starzl initially limited the transplantation to patients under age forty-five. Anticipating more such operations in the future, Starzl said surgeons need better tools and especially an antirejection medication specifically involving the digestive system. (At the time of Pittsburgh's announcement of successful abdominal transplantation, about eleven hundred people with malignant tumors had undergone liver, kidney, heart, or bone-marrow transplants worldwide, but none had multiple organ replacement.) Some transplant surgeons are of the persuasion that cancer metastasizes so swiftly and can hide so successfully when it does that the abdominal transplant will never be the cure of choice except as a last-ditch, desperation effort.

A few weeks later it was announced that Jack Fisher, a forty-six-year-old cardiomyopathy patient in Pittsburgh's Presbyterian-University Hospital awaiting a heart transplant, had set a record by spending his one hundred and seventh day with an electric blood pump working for his bad heart. This twenty-four-ounce plastic pump (Novacor) was implanted as a temporary means of assisting the left ventricle, which does the greatest percentage of the heart's work. The implanted pump causes no pain and does not require the bad heart to be removed to operate effectively. As this is written, however, the Novacor device requires not only electrical wires protruding from the patient's heart but some twenty feet of cable connected to a 440-pound console and computer that monitor the patient's heart rate; it controls the pump and must accompany the patient wherever he goes. The apparatus also makes a noticeably loud sound, but it's acceptable because, as Fisher was quoted, "if this stops clicking, I'm in trouble."

Bypass surgery, valve replacement, pacemaker implants to regulate heartbeats, angioplasty—these have become successful coronary therapy procedures. Bypass surgery started as early as the mid-1950s and is now done increasingly; thousands of sufferers with blocked coronary arteries have gone through the open-heart operation that presumes to correct these defects. But many cardiac conditions that only a few years ago required surgical bypass are now treatable with forms of coronary catheterization not requiring bypass surgery. Balloon angioplasty, introduced in 1977 by a Swiss doctor and used as treatment for patients with blockage in the coronary arteries, has become more and more reliable and is now recognized in many cases as a valid replacement procedure for bypass surgery. Balloon angioplasty is somewhat like the coronary diagnostic catheterization (arteriogram) process. First, as in the arteriogram, a catheter is inserted, generally in the femoral artery, in the groin area where that artery lies close to the skin. (The procedure is sometimes referred to as PTCA, percutaneous transluminal coronary angioplasty.) On reaching the heart, a dye is injected through the catheter, and by means of X ray, the narrowing segment of the artery (from atherosclerotic plaque buildup) is located. A soft guide wire with a small cylindrical balloon attached is inserted and moved to the blocked area; the balloon is inflated and then pushed through the narrow portion of the artery as often as necessary, opening the artery so that a nearly normal flow of blood, with its life-giving oxygen, is restored.

Balloon angioplasty is effective in most of the cases where it is tried. Since it is seldom attempted if atherosclerosis has involved too many arteries or where total blockage has taken place, the success rate of the procedure has improved to a point where some 90 percent of the patients are not only greatly relieved but do not suffer a return of the blocking substance (restenosis). Use of angioplasty has advantages over bypass surgery: It has been found that as many as 44 percent of bypass corrections are not permanent. Clogging of the coronary arteries usually continues so that in some cases, after eight to ten years, the operation must be repeated. (On the other hand, I have known bypass people whose reconstruction work was holding up after fifteen, even eighteen years, and their life-style hadn't suffered.) Balloon angioplasty does not involve a lengthy hospital visit, either. Sometimes it can be done with only an overnight stay. As in any intrusive procedure, however, coronary damage and death can result, so it is not something to be waltzed into without expert advice. The procedure is not often needed or useful to the cardiomyopathy patient, who is victim of a dying muscle not a clogged artery. (Balloon angioplasty is also used to open arteries other than coronary arteries, but that's another part of the forest.)

A newer procedure is coronary atherectomy, which removes plaque that is clogging a coronary artery. According to a Mayo Clinic Health Letter, the blockage is removed by use of a catheter that contains a tiny rotating cutting blade. A guide catheter (similar to that used for the coronary biopsy or the arteriogram) is positioned within a blocked artery, and the atherectomy catheter is then introduced by means of a fine wire. A metal cylinder containing a blade that spins at twenty-five hundred revolutions per minute is located an inch from the end of the catheter, and through a tiny window the rotating head shaves off the plaque and forces the shavings into a collection chamber that can be emptied and then reinserted. A tiny balloon pushes the cutting window against the artery's plaque-coated wall and prevents shavings from blocking the artery downstream. Only a small number of persons had undergone the procedure at the time the health letter was published, but it was noted that initial results "indicate that (the procedure) has great promise . . . successful in almost 90 percent of cases where patients had blocked coronary arteries."

The use of laser in treating coronary artery problems will probably become standard procedure, but at present there are problems with it; for example, a beating heart causes coronary arteries to move continually, making it most difficult to control the laser beam site without damaging the artery.

While bypass, valve replacement, and heart transplant all utilize the same surgical entrance procedures, leaving the same incision in the chest, bypass rehabilitation can be more painful than the other processes because in most bypass operations veins are taken from other parts of the patient's body, ordinarily the groin or the legs. This can and usually does give more after-pain than the surgery itself, but within rational limits, bypass patients can return to what we generally think of as normal living. Few need to continue on long-term medication the way transplant patients must. The bypass operation may be abused or overused, as some cardiologists have charged, but it can deliver saving relief.

How about performing bypass surgery on a transplanted heart? History's first was done in 1989 by surgeons at University Medical Center, Tucson, Arizona. The fifty-nine-year-old woman who had the double bypass received her transplanted heart in 1979, the fourth person to receive a heart at the Arizona center, and at the time of her unique bypass operation was the longest survivor among the 125 heart transplants done there. The seven-and-one-half-hour bypass surgery was felt necessary to help her after "life-threatening heart disease" was discovered. She was reported talking and sitting up in bed twenty-four hours later. (In all the news of changes and advancements in coronary treatment, I haven't heard of a transplanted heart being retrieved and put into a third body, but I don't see why it couldn't be done, given the proper parameters of age and physical environments.)

I include these developments not to update medical details (I would have to do a chapter a month in that case) but because they are typical of the advances being made in the field. Undoubtedly such advances will continue on a quite frequent basis—at least for the next few years as transplantation moves from pioneering to accepted protocol. The first announcements of a dramatic experiment are usually couched in cautionary phrases—sometimes Dr. Starzl's announcements are less so—but in many cases, the procedures quickly become less experimental and sometimes within weeks are being used in dozens of other programs.

Nevertheless, medical science, for all its specificity, retains many areas of the unknown, the unmeasured, the unpredictable. Healing and the duration of effectiveness for medication and the usefulness or the need of procedures all fall within that category. Doctors as a group tend to suspect advances that *might* take place. Too many cures for cancer and the common cold have been announced. Some reject advances that *have* taken place. This is not true of *all* doctors, but it is true of too many; there is always a generation of physicians, just as there is always a generation of academics, that does not want to learn too much more about its chosen field or subject. It can be quite comfortable practicing and teaching from the same positions that were learned while getting through an internship or leaving graduate school, and quite annoying to have to redo one's syllabus. It is turf protection if nothing else. Some doctors are reluctant to budge from one set of ominous predictions made on the first of the year even though such predictions no longer hold true at the end of the year.

Someone might ask: With so many advances being made in the field, is a potential organ transplant patient apt to encounter this kind of thinking? Unfortunately, the answer is: More often than one might expect. Except those rare physicians who hold a lively curiosity about all branches of healing, few keep up with even a handful of the advances that surge through the medical world on an almost daily basis. Other physicians, while willing to learn, are loyal to a private interpretation of Hippocrates' commandment—*Primum non nocere* (First, do no harm)—and hesitate to accept differing ideas or opinions.

I have never known a heart transplant patient who regretted having gone through the procedure or would refuse to do it again, although I am sure such exist, but despite these advances and exciting new procedures, the need for psychological support among all open-heart surgery patients remains great. And increasingly the medical world seems to be recognizing this. A good many doctors, while not scorning psychosomatic and psychological approaches, have refused or failed to recognize how important such approaches can be to the individual patient. It is understandable that to most M.D.s medication and specific procedures take precedence over psychological treatment (or however one classifies it), but denying the extreme position of "it's *all* in your mind" doesn't prove that *none* of it is in your mind. A newer generation of cardiologists and researchers declares that the psychological welfare and post-op social adjustment of most open-heart surgery patients (which includes both transplant and bypass patients) need more attention.

Who can say where transplantation will lead? Who could have predicted even a few decades ago that the process would advance to where it is? Medical scientists are still struggling to find a cure or a containment for many kinds of diseases and conditions that have been studied for years, and it would be foolish to predict that no such cures will ever be found, just as it would have been foolish to have predicted that no new terminal diseases would erupt in modern times when something like acquired immune deficiency syndrome (AIDS) makes a sudden, deadly entrance. So although many projections seem far-fetched to us now and most of us won't be around to see them put into effect, we can make some basic suppositions. Having gone through the "miracle" of transplantation and having seen it become somewhat less wondrous and more predictably routine, I am perhaps more inclined to play with the future than most. What next? Or is there a what next?

I asked a young Dallas surgeon if he thought the brain itself could someday be transplanted, and he said some portions *might* be adapted to a recipient but it just didn't seem possible at this time. When I suggested (with a bit of humor, please) that, if anything, it might be easier to transplant the entire head rather than just the brain, he agreed—and again, with a bit of humor, not science. He felt, as a surgeon, that detaching a brain imposed much more de-tailed work than detaching (and reattaching, of course) a head. Keeping the donor's system alive would be the first problem, regard-less of surgical advancement to the point that invisible nerves and other microchips of human intelligence could be isolated and trans-ferred. It certainly couldn't be done with even the most advanced "suture surgery" of today.

And think what a revolution in tradition, legend, romance, and religion there would be if, indeed, it became possible to transplant the brain. Would the new owner also receive the mind and skills and capabilities of the old owner? And, ethically speaking, would the decisions and convictions of the former owner transfer? What about all the things of which the heart is supposedly the seat? Although we

know they don't "transfer" with *that* organ, could we not assume
they would transfer with the brain?

Of course, just as tradition puts the soul in the heart, it puts the
mind in the brain. We must remember, however, the mind is not
an organ, it is a spirit, a process or condition. "Intelligent power,"
Shakespeare called it (quoted as a definition by Samuel Johnson in
his *Dictionary of the English Language* [1768] and Noah Webster
in his 1806 *Compendious Dictionary*). And there's the modern unabridged dictionary definition of mind: "an organized group of
events in neural tissue occurring mediately in response to antecedent
intrapsychic or extrapsychic events which it perceives, classifies,
transforms, and coordinates prior to initiating action whose consequences are foreseeable to the extent of available information."

Another surgeon, unconnected with the first, said he could see a
time not that far off when limbs and maybe muscles would be
routinely adapted from human to human. Or possibly more important, human organs and limbs will be "rebuilt" for cosmetic as well
as noncosmetic purposes. Certain kinds of toes, for example, will be
removed or reshaped, nasal passages undeviated, aural receptors improved, and eyes strengthened and lens deformities corrected early
in life as a matter of course, much like babies and young children
routinely receive inoculations and, in needed cases, certain corrective
surgery. Maybe someday the human body will be studied, nonsurgi-
cally dissected under the control of some to-be-invented kind of
machine, and the need for removal, transplantation, and correction
discovered and automatically placed at birth or soon after. For that
matter, much may take place in the womb—accepting, for the moment, that the womb will still be the organ of choice in human
production.

Or maybe there will come a time—sooner than we might predict—when the "perfect physical specimen" can be cloned or fabricated one part or segment at a time. The only thing standing in
the way (futuristically speaking) is the mortality of body parts. What
is the longest possible lifetime of human organs, bones, tissue, and
such? Will even that perfect physically fabricated specimen fall apart
as its parts begin to age? (Or is there to be a cure for old age?) And
all this overlooks the distinct probability that artificial or cloned parts
will be developed to a point where other human donors will not be

needed for many procedures; one may grow one's own parts by
cellular cloning. We may think now that cellular cloning would be
done "for medical uses only," but the way the world is, I forecast
nonmedical and cosmetic use will burgeon despite possible dangers,
the same way anabolic steroid use burgeoned when it was thought
to promote physical athletic prowess.

Or will we raise specific animals, say, baboons, for slaughter as we
do hogs and cattle for their usable parts?

Organ transplantation is not only an astonishing lifesaving field,
it has extended research into regions hitherto limited to medical
fantasy. The development of drug therapy is a good example. While
the use of cyclosporine has been great with transplantations, this is
not the only area in which its experimentation is taking place. Anyone familiar with the symptoms of AIDS can immediately see that
some of the deliberately induced immune suppressant processes bear
a certain likeness to the involuntary processes of AIDS. Therefore,
working a kind of back azimuth thinking, if involuntary immune
response can be controlled and the vulnerability of the organ transplant recipient lessened, couldn't something be done as a result to
reverse AIDS? Cyclosporine has been very helpful in cases of psoria-
sis, juvenile diabetes, and some forms of arthritis, although at this
writing still in the experimental stage.

What about the ethics of the whole transplant process? Won't
that have to change so that there is no moral or ethical quandary in
assigning organs (life) to one or another candidate? Well, as St.
Matthew recorded the Master saying, "Sufficient unto the day is the
evil thereof." When science and civilization have progressed past
previously accepted boundaries, mankind has nearly always found a
way to accommodate the advance. And in those rare instances in
which such an advance was refused, such as poison gas or nuclear
warfare, progress has not stopped, nor has it been shunted off to a
sidetrack. Civilization has found other ways to accomplish the same
thing. So if we are transplanting brains and heads someday we will
either have first found a way to accept this deviation from the history
of mankind or we will not use it. And remember, only a scant handful
of years back, even the attempt at transplanting the human heart was
held by some to be a sacrilegious act.

Today, in experiments around the world, uninjured body parts of various animals have been swapped—hands and fingers of baboons and monkeys—and I am sure such experiments are taking place in the United States, as has been evidenced in certain medical seminars and closed presentations—although I don't want to get involved in the question of "animal rights" by expressing approval or disapproval of those projects. The implanting of mammary glands of human females will surely be attempted, not for cosmetic purposes (inorganic implants already succeed), but in cases of certain diseases or abnormal conditions. A Chinese doctor, known for his experiments in transplant procedures, claims to have transplanted testicles to overcome physical sexual dysfunction. Readers old enough to have been reading newspapers and magazines or listened with sufficiently mature ears to the radio back in the 1930s may recall the career of Dr. John R. Brinkley, of Kansas and Texas fame, who owned one of the high-wattage border stations just across the Rio Grande, his microphone chats according him fame worldwide; he was called, informally and unofficially, "the Goat-Gland Man," having performed an operation similar to (but utilizing different lab animals) the one that was performed successfully by the Chinese surgeon. Although Brinkley's success rate was trumpeted as phenomenal, very few of his patients came forward to witness on his medical behalf—which is not so surprising if one thinks about it.

Some of the automatic trauma inherent in transplantation prior to the mid-1980s apparently has been dealt with either by change in prescription balance or through surgical advances. While transplantation will never be attempted on what might be called a casual basis, its awesomeness seems to be dissipating. The lack of donor organs still keeps it from being a common operation, but resistance on the part of the endangered seems to be lessening. And by the time an M.D. has tracked a patient from first symptoms to that safe year following transplantation, he has acquired not only a great deal of new medical knowledge but has gained a fund of understanding about the transplant process, so that advice and referrals can be based on current events, not leftover hearsay.

One reason one can be so certain that advances will be made in the transplantation field is the history of transplantation, of the drugs, procedures, and mechanisms associated with it—not to mention the doctors, surgeons, and lab workers who continued to develop, sometimes against tremendous peer group pressure, the successful processes that we enjoy today, processes that have added years to the lives of several thousand people. Our conception of healing, curing, and enhancing life through medical advances is enormously changed. It can almost be attributed to a genetic alteration, a readjustment of all human perception: reversing, rejecting, or overturning views and beliefs held for thousands of years or accepted truisms so deeply embedded in traditional culture that time has no meaning.

The human condition: The meaning of life never changes because it is internal, not external. The deepest meaning of life has not changed since the caveman's days, but the way we interpret experience can change, just as certain religions have had to make subtle shifts in the face of mechanical and theoretical science—not shifts of meaning but shifts of interpretation. In this regard I am reminded of an amusing, though sincere, misconstruction of a biblical verse that took place during World War II when automobile tires were rationed. Someone found a warning in the Bible against "head-tires" and immediately interpreted it as a prediction applicable to the 1939–45 war. The fact that the head-tires mentioned were spoken of thousands of years before automobile tires were thought of, and described hair ornaments, meant little to the literalists.

A small item in a newspaper column reported that in 1863 the chief surgeon of the United States National Heart Institute (though that sounds suspiciously early for such an agency) hung the following plaque on his wall: Let no man who hopes to retain the respect of his medical brethren dare to operate on the human heart.

With the staggering differences 130 years or so since have made, why quail at the differences 130 years or so ahead will surely bring?

Chapter 7

In the earliest days of heart transplants, when it was little more than an exotic news item to me, I was like most healthy persons; when I read about them my first response was, "Thank God, I'll never have to have one" and I hadn't thought about a heart transplant being the answer even after I discovered I had heart problems. The operation was still considered risky, a 40–60 or even 30–70 odds-against proposition. Only when I faced the crucial decision no one but me could make, life or death, did I accept the thought that a heart transplant was the only preference possible, but in any case it was a preference.

The expansion of organ transplant methods and opportunities has become as *vital* to survival and modern medicine as anything since the various discoveries of blood and oxygen functions, of hygienic methods and surgical techniques. It combines them, certainly, but then delivers a product never contemplated except as fantasy.

What does the word "vital" mean? It means, in simplest terms, life. Vital organs are those necessary to the maintenance of life—not the source of our humanity nor of our love or laughter or sorrow, but of our life. The vital organs are the pumps, the filters, the mechanical control boxes of human existence. They are to the human body what the engine is to the automobile. When the automobile's engine does not operate, you have a ton or more of specially shaped steel, rubber, and plastic worth little more than $150, if that. When the vital organs are not operating, you have a reasonably large, specifically shaped heap of fat, skin, bones, and some other chemicals (which, after a few nonoperational minutes, must be kept on ice to have any value) worth between $28 and $128, according to how many gold teeth that collection boasts. That is why the development of organ transplantation over the recent decades is so fascinating. It gives meaning to abstract values . . . it means life.

Just as you take your automobile into the repair shop from time to time to get an engine tune-up or other maintenance, so we do with our bodies. And just as some automobiles continue to run well past the ordinary limits of use, such as 50,000 to 150,000 miles, so do some humans. An automobile needs lights, glass, paint, and, for the finest use, air conditioning, radios, cigar lighters, electronic monitoring systems—but if the engine dies, none of them matter.

Learning that you have heart trouble of any kind is a little like finding out something baffling has happened to your automobile: not a flat that, while stopping progress, can be fixed; and not running out of fuel, which can be amended with a phone call or a hitchhike to a filling station. But when an automobile stops completely or develops some alarming signal that even the least mechanically minded motorist recognizes as potentially disastrous, then you grow fearful; you may lift the hood and stare at the dead or dying mechanism, or possibly you huddle inside the car, rattled, afraid, not knowing what is wrong or what will have to be done. Even if the mechanic tells you what is wrong inside the engine and says repair is possible, you fear that the machine is ruined and you cannot trust it anymore. This failure metaphor may sound mechanistic, but that's what heart trouble actually is: a mechanical failure.

There are parts of the human body that greatly assist life but do not support it. Yes, we want to run up a decent mileage figure, to keep our limbs intact; yes, we want to be able to see well all our life, and hear well and taste our food and have hair on our heads and enjoy sex after sixty—but we can live without these things. They are not vital. They are not life. The heart, the liver, the lungs, the kidneys . . . they are. In rare cases they can continue to function with marginal operating capacity, but they must continue to function at some level, with some percentage of efficiency. Not even the brain is so necessary to continued existence.

The constant question for the potential transplant candidate is, "How long do I have?" It can't be answered with any certainty, but the worst answer anyone can be given is, "Unknown." Even a shaky guess, with a few parameters of hope, of course, is superior to "Unknown."

Even though I had been turned down by one major transplant program this negative fact was not allowed to take over my prognosis. Was Bill Kraus, the physician, offering unbelievable assurance during this time, assurance he doubted himself? No, he was not. I think it is most important (and this is a personal point, not necessarily one everyone would embrace) that one's doctor, particularly one's cardiologist, should be straightforward but not gloomy in attitude. Honest, yes; Bill Kraus pointed out the pitfalls of every step I was to take toward every decision I made. He also kept himself professionally up to date—not easy today, even for a specialist—so that he could assist me in making those decisions.

Without pointing a finger at any cardiologist, I hear of some who, even after years of successful heart transplantation with its accompanying advances, seem to be thinking in 1970s terms, viewing the procedure as something dangerously experimental, ineffective, and an uneven gamble. I heard from one undecided cardiomyopathy patient whose cardiologist said a heart transplant, even if successful, would not necessarily prolong life and would degrade the quality of the survivor's life, at best. The patient asked if my doctor had told me that; I laughed (somewhat bitterly) and said if he had I would have dropped him, that prolongation of life was the foremost reason for taking the plunge. "Prolong" can cover days or years, but it means more life, using anybody's calendar.

Presuming I was admitted to some transplant program, did the almost legendary high cost of the operation concern me? It certainly did. I had had an appendectomy and a later-in-life tonsillectomy several years back but no experience with major operations and costly procedures in more modern terms. I had read that any transplant operation was extremely costly, and my personal income was scarcely a jot or tittle on the suggested sums. I also was not sure that my medical insurance coverage was sufficient to see me through the medical and hospital portions of that initial operation cost, much less the sustaining months after the transplant if it was successful, if I recuperated; and there was the ordeal of not knowing how long I might survive. While I had a good job and some added income from various forms of authorship, a sizable deviation from my budget would be economically disastrous. But what was the alternative? Since the alternative was unthinkable, I didn't let myself think about costs or about the downside because that can be the most debilitating part of a lengthy illness or of an unscheduled, unpredictable waiting period.

Even at the point where I realized I was weakening each day and must have a heart transplant or die, I was not willing to give up all professional activities. I know it sounds foolish or self-important, and I suppose it was, but I felt I still had too many stories, columns, and books to write, videos to tape, speeches to make, whether they hindered survival or not. I wasn't assuming that everything I had to do was earthshaking, but I did feel a sort of obligation to my self-image not to have too many loose ends dangling, whether departing for the hospital or the hereafter. And while this may come as a surprise to them, I didn't want to leave family, friends, and associates feeling that I had failed them. I wanted their pride in my ability to survive to be reinforced by my actions, at least to a point of quiet satisfaction. Of course it was false bravery, and I recognized it as such, but it is hard to educate the human to demise. Death just isn't one of mankind's favored schools.

Still, I recognized (or thought I recognized) the physical danger my attitude of "work, work" implied. As daily life and my career became harder and more complicated, I had to restrain myself from pushing to the wall in the urgency of my impatience. If my bad heart deteriorated further, my liver, lungs, kidneys, or pancreas could become irreversibly damaged, and a heart transplant could be negated.

Though he begged me to drop the idea, I told Bill Kraus I would continue teaching through the fall semester of 1987. It was a matter of honor. (How many of us sacrifice our lives and our happiness gambling on that absurd or false proposition?) The university was willing for me not to teach; in fact, Jim Lee insisted I not, but I insisted more tenaciously that I should.

On campus in Denton, I walked upright but rested every thirty yards or so. At home in Dallas, I lumped down in a reclining swivel chair, and I do mean *lumped.* Friends and coworkers could see how disabled I was. I'm sure most of them thought I was being foolishly brave or just foolish. Some told me later that they never expected to see me alive again. It wasn't true bravery that kept me going, it was hardheadedness and spiritual determination. And I hate to admit it wasn't strength of character alone that motivated a lot of that determination; it was income. But need for income can be a strong factor in bravery and determination.

As that autumn aged, my hours became an undefined blur, not from passing swiftly but merely going from one dawn to the next without anything interceding. No way to assume new hope, no way to look back in expectation of learning something useful for the future, and no real way to look forward, either—only a way to look *at,* to sit or stand, and wait. I tried several kinds of what might be called "experimental" heart drugs, tried them hopefully and in most cases with a great deal of faith that if there was any way possible that they could work I would *make* them work. They may have worked on my psychology, but they didn't work on my physiology. My heart continued to die.

Even now, over two years later, I discover things I did that fall of which I have only the vaguest recollection. In November I went on a filming expedition to West Texas with Bill Mercer of the university's television, radio, and film school, his wife, Jim Lee, and Fran Vick, the newly appointed director of the University of North Texas Press. We filmed at various places of interest and later were joined by Lawrence Clayton, dean of Hardin-Simmons University, and his wife, and the next day the UNT crew got up early (according to my journal) and we filmed everything from cotton fields to the railroad station at Abilene, then had supper at the Lambshead Ranch. I don't remember more than a dozen frames of all that action. If it weren't for some surviving video footage, I would almost deny it had taken place. (The filming was wasted, incidentally. I looked so bad and my voice was so quavery that the project was abandoned.)

• • •

Questions flooded my mind even while it was working frantically to escape questions. Have they forgotten about me? Are the doctors partial? Or are they prejudiced against me? Fear of dying, of wearing out, before a heart can be found afflicts the cardiomyopathy victim, while in the case of coronary disease patients it is fear that another attack, another stroke, another spasm—anything twitching, hurting, tingling—will sweep them away. Life becomes a melancholy circus. "Heart attack" victims feel as though they are walking a slippery tightrope, while congestive heart failure patients feel they are falling without a net to doom. Fear that they will die before a suitable heart is found is more likely in cases of heart disease victims, many of whom must live in the hospital for weeks or even months, surviving new attacks and heart stoppages. Cardiomyopathy becomes a deadening, wasting process with no solacing condition available. The passing of time is not one more day alive, it is one more day toward death. For the would-be transplantee, waiting to be admitted to the heart list and then waiting for an organ are the most dangerous times. Beyond the medical and physical difficulties, the biggest danger is from the mind. Yeats wrote: "Hearts are not had as a gift but hearts are earned." Being denied an admittance, did that mean I had somewhere, somehow, failed to earn a heart, was unworthy of a good one? Would never get a *new* one?

You can come down with "waiting" as if it were a disease—which it is. Depression is another name for it. After a few weeks, the "waiter"—the one waiting for a heart—becomes a different person. I thought I was too strong to succumb to nervous fears or too experienced to let clock-watching make me tremble, but all that certainty dissolved. One morning, for example, I woke up and decided I couldn't continue my marriage even though it had lasted happily for more than thirty-seven years. The "trembles" had me wobbling. By the next day the idea was as foreign as Sanskrit. Women who are waiting may feel the guilt of neglect, not neglect of themselves but of their children or their husbands or household duties or friends. And, of course, the male faces many of these same arrows of guilt while he sits or slowly dissolves, economic helplessness crippling his resolve.

Several other heart patients have told me they shared my uneasy twinges of guilt at becoming crippled and helpless, even though family members and friends might take great pains to persuade us they had no such concerns, that the only prevailing thought on their minds was our survival, not their own inconvenience. But the person slumped in the chair, whether householder, wage earner, or guardian of family affairs, can't help assuming some kind of blame, having spent week after week of unproductive waiting, thinking everything—the family circle, the job, the community of friends—is going to collapse "and I will be the cause of it"; thus, "I must not be worthy of a good heart."

The sour sentiment of "I know they hate me" can become the recurring conviction of every day that doesn't bring some small triumph or encouraging word—and in the chairbound state, few days do.

You never know, of course, what is going through the mind of another, even when "another" is your spouse or your offspring. One cardiomyopathy patient, awaiting a heart, told me he knew that his friends and family had more trouble dealing with this slow, degenerative time than he did. An older Roman Catholic priest, whom I came to know in a cardiac program, said one of the greatest aids to hanging on during his especially lengthy wait for a donor heart was hearing from successful cardiac transplantees who could track every week of his frustration and his impatience because they had been there. In my own case, the first heart transplant veteran I ever met, some months before I was an official candidate, was Ben Dial of the Stanford program, and his cheery reaction to his new heart was one of the most heartening (!) experiences I had. Other transplantees, mostly those having had coronary artery diseases, say they needed the added assurance of someone they trusted, someone who would be able to handle things in case they had cardiac arrest and had to live in a hospital or were forced to become bedfast.

Not all families are able to keep up the pace (or the farce, if you will) of sympathy and understanding; the further the time stretches, the faster impatience runs. Many friends and family members can grow to hate the person in the chair, though the hatred is temporary in most cases (especially if, ironically enough, the patient later receives a heart—or dies), blaming that sick person for the things they think and do. They express this hostility by an air of absence-in-spirit or by separation through distancing, whether across town, from one room to another, or only a matter of a few feet as they pass before or around the enthroned, disabled, waiting figure—a figure strange and not always recognizable, even though only a few months or weeks ago it was beloved and as warm and close as memory.

And if this distancing is not evident—in fact, does not exist—does the person in the chair acknowledge the loyalty and calm acceptance of those around him? Not always, I hate to say. Although I feel this was not one of my real sins during my waiting period, my own journal reflects some of this. At a point when my family was devoting many hours per week trying to make me comfortable in mind and body, I wrote, "Felt pretty good—physically, that is—but psychologically I'm getting very down." At another point, after I had tried rather fruitlessly to work on my tax problems, I complained, "Worn out deep down—the IRS will kill me if my children don't beat 'em to it!" One Saturday I noted that "none of the kids" called or visited, but the next time one did I told myself he "visited, but [was] noncommital to N—— and J—— and me." This feeling of isolation can become so strong that it may overwhelm other emotions, even good sense.

The attitude of "they must hate me," while seldom expressed directly, sometimes reaches such a point that the tiniest crease in the affairs of those around the patient, the minute hesitations or indirect sighs, shove him directly into the tumbling terror of, "Oh, my God, they're sick of me, they're just putting on a brave face . . . they all wish I would die." It is hard, damned hard, to think about the present when it is such a nebulous thing.

Betty had contracted for some necessary home repairs shortly after I left the hospital following a pneumonia bout, and although I saw the need for the work, more and more I resented the workmen and (I cringe to admit) her along with them. In a little seizure of frustration I described a late spring day: "Didn't feel very perky . . . will be so glad when this work is over. I'm wanting to go *on*. I can't be held up by this kind of inconvenience. I need the time, I've got so much to do." The truth was, I had nothing to do, could do nothing but wait on a heart.

And as for planning toward the future—well, even my cheerful wife couldn't always bring herself to do that. And my children stayed off the subject as though they were plotting a death. And maybe they were. Not consciously but sort of, you know, thinking, If Dad's going to die, why make his lingering hours fake and fraudulent? They were caught, as so many concerned persons are, between overattention and neglect; overattention emphasizing the fear they dare not show ("Why is everybody being so damned agreeable? You think I'm going to die?") but neglect, for them, being out of the question. Of course I was wrong. None of it was taking place—at least not on their part—and I tried hard not to let myself slump into a persistent mental whine. My family tried as hard as they could, without consultations or conferences, to keep me hopeful, to go beyond hope even if (and I'm sure this was true) they felt less and less of it.

Self-pity is an occupational hazard of the sick, and it can sweep over its victim with the same speed and impairment as a disease. Death, especially inevitable death, can become a romantic vision—a delusory challenge to choose it or life. I know. As my seventh month of waiting for a heart began I wrote, almost hopefully, "I don't feel nearly as optimistic as I did last week. . . . I feel as if I am dying, I'm so worn out." Strong as I believed myself to be—and I was verging on obnoxious in that regard—it eventually afflicted me. I never reached the point where I *wanted* to die, but as the poet Keats mused, I found myself "half in love with easeful Death . . . to cease upon the midnight with no pain." And after a series of sharp verbal encounters with a son (and Betty so worn out she had to go to the hospital for two days), I confessed to myself, "I hardly stirred from my green swivel chair all day; am very despondent over a heart; when are they going to find an O-type? I'm getting to the point . . . I really scarcely care if more of this is all I have to look forward to." I began to doubt myself emotionally and professionally: "Feeling physically better but emotionally bad. Just how good a writer am I?"

Why would anyone feel romantic about approaching death? Because it may become an easier choice, even in the face of assurances and support? The loss of hope creates a kind of spiritual hallucination, and within this mirage, death seems preferable to continued existence. I began to dream dreams and see visions, allowing myself the thought that the world and I would both be better off with me out of it. This may sound unreal, but with enough time spent in a chair or on one's back—or perhaps not even confined—it can seem a reasonable alternative.

There are times when all of us think or maybe say that we are ready to die, to give up this pointless vigil, just as there are times when we stand beside our disabled automobile and wish there were some way to dispatch the beast, to shoot it or, if nothing more, push it into a ditch and proceed by foot. Panic is the first villain one encounters in the heart-pilgrim's progress, and overcoming it may very well mean the difference between finishing the journey and going only a few more paces. Terror lurks near any threatening episode. It resides just beneath the surface of every medical examination, every test or measurement. But so does death. And to let them get in sight of each other, if only for a moment, is the skirmish that sometimes loses the war.

Yet expectations of some Great Unknown beyond death beckon hauntingly to one who is scarcely hanging on to the known. And there is denial of even this hope—the Great Unknown—if one presumes there are no feelings beyond the abruptness of dying. So after a spell it becomes easy to persuade oneself that nothing is *unknown* simply because no *known* has been revealed. Depending more on miracles than on medicine, those on beds of affliction (for whom my father used to offer many a supper table prayer) may find it hard not to accept dying as *the* final definition.

Biographer Jean Strouse, speaking of Alice James (sister of William and Henry), said that late in life when Miss James's cancer was diagnosed, the sister wrote William that the approach to death "was the most supremely interesting moment in life. . . . I have a delicious consciousness, ever present, of wide spaces close at hand and whispers of release in the air." And Ms. Strouse notes, "Alice somewhat ironically assumed His providence." Her biographer calls Alice James "a neurasthenic . . . who spent most of her life suffering from mysterious ailments . . . systematically closing down every option that might have led her away from a life of invalidism . . . turning into a tyrannical invalid who collapsed in order to get people to take care

of her." This is a rather damning summation, but such invalidism
can also be taken to a point where it must be recognized. One of the
greatest challenges of medicine or psychiatry is making people well
who don't think they want to be well, who like it better in the
invalid's role or, more romantically speaking, as death's doomed
quarry: "the most supremely interesting moment in life."

That sounds like the image a great many of us, when waiting on
hearts, either have of ourselves or think others have of us. But, thank
heavens, it is an image that is usually swept away in the realization
of our new heart once it is functioning in place. The important thing
for the heart patient to convince himself of is staying alive by whatever means, even if in some cases medical means have proved incapa-
ble of the job. And it can be difficult, especially if you decline to the
point that you can't do anything creative or useful, if you have to give
up everything but looking and thinking. Religious faith is an important part of many survivals and recoveries, but it is an individual
concern, and its effectiveness, I feel, is not something on which one
bases public predictions.

Sigmund Freud proclaimed, "The ego is not master in its own
house," and several generations took that edict and tried to live with
it in an existential pattern that looked reasonable on the outside but,
like a bruised melon, was less enticing once peeled. Motive can be
stronger than ego. Motive can be controlled; ego can't ("But I just
can't *help* it!"). But for those facing the demands of actuality,
control becomes superior to, or at least the equal of, ego. Motive can
save us. Our insides, whether referring to the belly or the brain, are
powerful and can lift us above extraordinary events or drown us with
the slightest wave. Every fear gets the response it demands of the
ego; only the tough motive can answer fear negatively.

But motivation *can* force the ego to surrender, *can* answer fear,
holding it in check as it lunges toward panic, and *can* calm stress as
well as appetite. Stress is not something you catch, it's not something
that comes over you like a migraine. It's not how you handle the
outside event, it is how you handle the unending bombardment of
outside events. Stress is a conditioned response and we all feel it. But,
like fear, it can be overcome by a strong enough motive. "I want to
live! I want to live with joy!" (This may sound as if it all came easily

and naturally to me, and I am now in a position to chide you if it doesn't do either, but believe me, stress, fear, and sagging motives dogged my trail, overtaking me almost as often as I outran them.)

Is any of this automatic? Not much. Is it possible? Not always. Is it useful? For someone facing the Final Reality, especially under prolonged terms, it is not only useful, it is imperative. To someone waiting for a heart (or whatever organ) or learning to live with a new heart—learning the discipline of diet, exercise, routines and medication; learning the metes and bounds of a completely changed lifestyle (no matter how much we may despise the word, as many do, including, I confess, me)—motivation is supreme. That is, if surviving is the paramount concern.

And it seems to me that someone who wants to make it through the waiting, through the trauma of the operation and hospital stay, surely must be motivated by survival at a high level. Looking back, I wish I had had more faith in God, in fate, or just in myself. It cost me too many anxious, uselessly lost hours. Maybe, as in the case of some, survival has dissolved into more dream than goal, and we are prone to accept whatever seems inevitable; but still, given a choice (which we have been offered and presumably accepted), we look to a future that should be slightly less cloudy than the immediate past, though less romantic than will-o'-the-wisp thoughts of meeting the Universal Comforter.

Today, after all that, after working, then waiting, almost too long, but after having a successful heart transplant, would I do it again? I would keep active but not hold on to my work blindly and with that "high moral principle" attitude I must have had, even if I didn't think so. Pushing to the wall, testing the envelope—any way you want to say it—is too dangerous. One month or one week of exertion may be too much. And if that happens, your chances of getting a heart in time or getting one at all diminish at a rate far faster than the work might be worth. Thus, looking back, no, I wouldn't wait for nature or my body to rebel and force me to do what common sense had every right to tell me earlier. Postoperative survival depends so much on the health of one's organs and internal environment that to damage any portion endangers all favorable prognoses.

Chapter 8

The first week of December 1987 as the fall semester finished at the university, Betty and I boarded a plane and flew to Houston where I entered St. Luke's Hospital to be tested by the Texas Heart Institute. I immediately felt "at home." Dr. Denton Cooley, head of the Institute, had corresponded with the staff some years before when I was executive editor of the *Southwestern Historical Quarterly* and a story on his transplantation experiments was projected. He rushed into my hospital room, shook my hand, and said, "I've been wanting to meet you," which made me feel better, not for the recognition but from the point of view of a sick stranger in a strange town. (Betty referred to him as "the handsome thing.") I had met Dr. Robert Hall, the medical coordinator of the program, three years before when I gave a historical tour of Dallas to a group of cardiologists and their wives. Then Dr. O. H. (Bud) Frazier, who would be my surgeon under the Institute program, turned out to be a student of Texas history who had collected several of my Texas books. During World War II he had been assigned to a small Army engineering training unit at John Tarleton Agricultural College, a state school in West Texas, my region of origin. One of his fellow trainees was Norman Shumway, who became head of transplant surgery at the famed Stanford University Center. Neither was an M.D. at the time, and certainly neither dreamed of becoming internationally recognized for performing an operation then considered more science-fictitious than scientific.

St. Luke's Hospital had achieved a fine reputation worldwide, and its heart transplant floor was not only well staffed and well run but cheerful in ways not usually associated with a hospital. The halls and rooms were carpeted (and I've never understood why more hospitals don't install carpeting), and the staff, from the surgeons, interns, surgical trainees, and registered nurses to the technicians and order-lies, was long-suffering, polite, and cheery when it was called for, and impressively knowledgeable. I also met, for the first time, groups of people who had gone through the transplant procedure and survived the near-death of their hearts.

On the other hand (and you have to say "on the other hand" so often in this life) I also met people who had come close to the end with coronary heart diseases, not congestive heart failure. Congestive heart failure is by no means the only reason for a heart transplant—or even the *main* reason. Most heart transplants have taken place *after* bypass and other correctional forms have been unsuccessful or have not held. Some bypass surgery has been preceded by instances of cardiac arrest, where the heart has had to be restarted, which is seldom the case with cardiomyopathy. Sometimes the condition of coronary disease patients becomes acute, and their hearts may stop several times prior to the transplant operation. However, the human side of heart transplantation is the same for heart disease and conges-tive heart failure victims, and the fears and frustrations of waiting for a donor heart are identical. After the operation, their prior dis-ability makes no difference in what transplant patients do, the medi-cations they take, or the clinical schedules they must meet.

Since I had been told I was possibly too old for a transplant, I was apprehensive on that point. (A Dallas surgeon reported me an unsuit-able candidate because I was "an old sixty-four.") But at St. Luke's I was assured by Drs. Frazier and Hall that if testing showed no critical organic conditions, age would not be a determining factor in my getting a heart transplant. I joked with Frazier about this, telling him I now understood why the age limit for heart transplants kept edging upward. Surgeons such as Cooley and Shumway at Stanford, and himself, were edging upward and had discovered that reaching sixty or so was not the end of life.

The first days of exhaustive testing wore me down; they were exhaustive in both uses of the word—I was in and out of my room for testing every thirty minutes to an hour. At one point I was transferred to the Intensive Care Unit when my blood pressure dropped, my potassium level was low, and I had what Dr. Hall termed "an ugly heartbeat." He decided the rigorous testing planned for the next two days would have to wait, and that suspended the decision as to my conformation for the heart transplant list. Finally, on the morning of December 16, the remaining tests were performed, and late that afternoon Kathy Vershaave, a transplant coordinator, came in to tell Betty and me that I had been accepted for the Texas Heart Institute transplant program and put on the heart list. Betty recorded both of our immediate reactions—reactions of joy and relief—when she wrote, "Hooray!" All I could do, in the meantime, was return to Dallas or move to Houston in order to wait for a suitable donor heart. I decided to return and wait in Dallas. And, becoming sicker and sicker, I began the most dismal, frustrating period in my life, a period I would not care to relive even knowing that a form of redemption awaited its end.

Houston being over 250 miles from Dallas, I was prepared to do whatever made the obtaining of a heart easier and quicker. I was ready to become a Houston resident for whatever period might be required. The Texas Heart Institute people agreed with my decision to wait in Dallas, thinking I would function better remaining at home for as long as possible. A great deal of helpfulness was displayed toward me for either decision. A Houston couple, longtime literary and political friends, offered my wife and me the use of a beautiful home in Houston, near St. Luke's, and a Dallas couple arranged for a private jet, on a twenty-four-hour basis, to take Betty and me there from Dallas when the call came that St. Luke's had a heart for me. Dr. Kraus volunteered to join us aboard the jet if the call came and began carrying around a bag with changes of clothing and toiletries. (If that sounds as if I have some privileged status, be assured it is only the privilege of friendship.) In Dallas, Betty and Meredith were equipped with beepers so they could be summoned if the heart call came while they were away. No need for me to carry a beeper (although many transplant patients do) because I wasn't going anywhere out of telephone range.

My children rallied around. My eldest, Geoffrey, his wife Arabella (who, I'm more than happy to say, has been as much daughter as daughter-in-law), and my youngest, Meredith, left careers in New York and moved to Dallas to join their brothers Eliot and Mark to be nearby when whatever happened happened. All were optimistic and supportive, contributing greatly to my sluggish survival. Some transplant centers require (or prefer) that patients have family or friends available in a supporting capacity, but some recent studies indicate this may not be necessary, that loners seem to make it through a transplant about as readily as those with friends and families.

I feel my family's involvement was a major part of my survival; I absolutely could not have made it during the long waiting and recuperating ordeals without my wife. And I question the idea that loners make it through transplants as well as others. Despite modern sociology's depiction of so many of us being lonely in a crowd or being part of the lonely crowd, the need for comforting reference remains. Who wouldn't feel safer and more certain having someone close and holding your hand as you emerge from the anesthetic or go to restless sleep some nights? And speaking peevishly and personally, I do get tired of having generally accepted ideas suddenly reversed, especially on the slender basis of an unnumbered "study" done by some unnamed institution. The ability to follow the medical program may be more important in the short term than family support, which makes sense because the inability to follow a program can end in disaster whether one has family support or not, but after the ebullience of coming through alive begins to wear off, loneliness can be as killing as medical reversal.

The transplant patient and his or her family members, waiting for a heart or any other organ, should be careful of their emotional "input." Patient handbooks given by most transplant programs can be scary to read because they tend to stress the expediencies of procedure, medication, and rejection probability. For example, most

handbooks, when describing cardiac biopsy procedure, sound unnerving ("inserting an instrument either through the neck or groin
vein into the right ventricular chamber of the heart and tak[ing] a
tissue sample") if they don't add that surface anesthetics or intrave-
nous pacifiers are, or can be, administered. Side effects of medication
often sound as threatening as whatever they are being given to cure,
ease, or contain, such as, "Cyclosporine use can cause liver and
kidney dysfunction, high blood pressure, increased susceptibility to
infection, trembling and shaking of the hands, headaches, leg
cramps, swollen gums, nausea, or vomiting." And the downside
effects of prednisone are genuinely frightening: "Osteoporosis, or
softening of the bones in the vertebrae and weight-bearing joints, is
possible. . . . Changes in physical appearance may occur; there is a
tendency to 'moonface.' . . . Cataracts may develop; a diabetic state
can be induced; 'Cushinging' [after the renowned Dr. Harvey Cush-
ing] with prominent upper-back fat deposits . . . oily skin may lead
to acne. . . ."

It is understandable, of course, that the would-be transplantee
must be warned about what *could* happen. And the persons writing
the handbooks are medical professionals to whom such procedures
and dire possibilities are common events. However, the possibility of
any one patient being hit by all or even a large number of these side
effects is slim. In the first place, no patient will receive every drug
as described or be subjected to every procedure, and what may be
a daily or weekly occurrence to the medical professional is a once-in-
a-lifetime episode to the patient.

The same cautious approach applies to some of the books written
about transplantation. While the book itself may be accurate, reader
interpretation can be misguided. For instance, in reviewing one
well-written publication, the otherwise qualified reviewer protested,
"I can say . . . that on balance organ transplantation is not worth it,
is not something I would wish on a dying relative." But to a transplantee, that is not the book's message at all. It only reads that way
to someone who has not been there or been familiar with someone
who has.

The dismal (and dismayed) view can seem justified unless you are
able to know a little more about the process. Frankly, I suggest that
a transplant candidate not read many technical or medical books on

the subject, no matter how accurate they may be. Some, in their caution to give the downside scenario, can create quite a scare in the nonmedical reader. For that matter it might be a good idea for the patient and immediate family not to read too much theory about transplantation until after they have been through it. Then reading about it and finding circumstances of similarity or familiarity on nearly every page can be exciting.

Bad luck or chance seemed to strike immediately once I finished being tested at the Texas Heart Institute. On the afternoon plane returning to Dallas from Houston that December day, I was so weak I lumped into my seat, only half conscious of being alive. I tried to get comfortable with an airline pillow, but I've never known this to be possible for a man, even a healthy man. I blamed my discomfort on the final pair of tests that had been done only that morning—tests that left my esophagus and stomach sore from the intrusion of a big plastic tube. The cabin attendant saved my life (I wish I had gotten her name) by volunteering to make me a cup of hot cocoa, which wasn't on the drink menu. Few things have ever tasted so good. Dallas was dismal, cold, and drizzly when Betty and I landed, and I more or less passed out in the car as our son Eliot drove us home. Then the first thing I saw when I walked in the front door of the house was a notice that the Internal Revenue Service was auditing a past tax return. I made it into a swivel chair and announced I wasn't moving. (Just to illustrate that life goes on, regardless of the *Sturm und Drang* associated with your immediate existence, during the months I was chairbound and then hospitalized, the IRS proceeded to audit not one but three years of my returns, finding me "guilty" to the tune of several thousand dollars but showing a degree of mercy by assigning part of the blame for my mistakes to my weakened physical condition at the time I was collecting tax data for Chuck Spicer, my CPA, and not penalizing me for evil intent or whatever legal phrase is used. Further evidence that life *must* go on as long as there's life, the first thing I did the day, months later, I returned home from the hospital with my new heart was confer for four hours on my tax problems with my CPA. When I survived that, Chuck and I agreed, I was likely to last.)

• • •

Still lumped out when Christmas came, I missed our traditional family dinner at the home of Betty's brother, Tom Dozier. Not only did I remain chairbound, but the thought of eating turkey, oyster dressing, giblet gravy, candied sweet potatoes, and ambrosia (all of which Taina, my Finnish sister-in-law, prepared to perfection) made me gag. Two days after Christmas, as I was coughing and aching and showing no sign of recovering from the Houston stay, Bill Kraus ordered me in for more testing at St. Paul Medical Center, and when Eliot showed him my sputum cup used during the short trip from home to the hospital, Dr. Kraus, without further ado, admitted me to ICU and began immediate treatment for lobar pneumonia, possibly the worst threat to a damaged heart.

Those three winter weeks in the hospital battling pneumonia pushed me close to the edge. Even today Bill Kraus says getting me through pneumonia was his greatest contribution to my survival. At first, rest alone carried me; then, in a few days, medication began restoring some vigor, and I was moved to a private room and withstood the testing procedures better. Eventually I was even able to have two liters of fluid drawn from my right lung by aspiration (or in plainer words, with a long needle).

I remember little of the first few days except that on New Year's Eve I watched from my hospital room window the tall, lighted building in the Southwestern Medical Center complex across the boulevard from me, where a large party of faculty and friends of Dr. Donald Seldin, then head of the school's internal medicine department, was celebrating at Donald and wife Muriel's traditional champagne and omelet party—a party I hadn't missed in seventeen years prior to that night. So near, yet so far. Sentimental? I suppose so. I became sentimental about a number of things those first pneumonia days. I could almost visibly see the past rushing away from me, and I seemed always to be on the verge of tears. Although I couldn't admit even to myself that I had any thought of death, fears and tears lurked within me nevertheless. I can look back and see that I was battling the thought of death and having to give up life before I was finished with it. And I had to keep reminding myself that strong men don't cry and are not sentimental.

There is something unpropitious about New Year's Eve for us

formerly stouthearted folks, something that makes us regretful or sad
or disappointed in ourselves. But whatever causes it, New Year's Eve
seems to be a bad time for people under The Threat. I have talked
to others, including a few doctors, and it seems to be fairly usual for
patients to regress on New Year's Eve. You would think that if
regression were indicated at any particular season it would be at
Christmas or Yom Kippur, Hanukkah, Valentine's Day—days of
memory. Maybe New Year's Eve becomes more oppressive because
it puts an end to a period that started out hopefully. The other
holidays offer happy memories—as does New Year's Eve, from the
purely entertaining standpoint—but we also put so much faith in the
future that officially starts the next day. And then, 364½ or so days
later, few of us have caught up with the pledges and expectations
from that previous time. And for someone under The Threat, that
hopelessness is magnified a thousand percent on New Year's Eve.
The next morning, New Year's Day, life may lift a little, things may
get back into a better focus, some kind of hope may be restored.
Outliving the old year becomes harder than living to greet the new
day. Perhaps you get overly sentimental at times of blind jeopardy
and the stress of not knowing or being able even to glimpse the
future. Nobody likes to walk into a strange, dark room. There is an
instant when, frantically and unsuccessfully searching for the light
switch, we are all seized with mankind's ancient fear of the unknown.

I didn't fear death as much as I feared not recovering my faculties,
my speech, my ability to think clearly or to talk (because during my
pneumonia period I became winded at something as simple as reading a paragraph or two aloud). I feared, even if I survived the pneumonia and, if it came, the transplant, that I would be an old man
in more ways than chronologically. This was my real fear, more than
of death, though death, of course, when you duel this proposition,
is always a spectator if not a participant. But find me another word
for fear, something slightly less shaking, something slightly more
definitive, but something a man can admit to holding without that
taint of shame; a less menacing term but still apprehensive: dismay?
Consternation? Trepidation?

The movie *All That Jazz* is about a man with many problems but
primarily (from the physical standpoint) a heart problem. It kills him,

more because of his attitude toward life—he was in love with death—than because of his heart. When I first saw the movie, I didn't conceive that I might have to go through something of the same thing as far as the operation shown was concerned (from the dialogue you assume it is a bypass). I stared at the screen with curiosity as the scalpel made the first delicate red-line slice down his chest—the incision that leads to "the zipper." I watched the cranking rib-spreader as it spread his ribs (I asked a doctor what the name of that appliance was that opened the chest, and he said it was called, with unaccustomed medical directness, "the rib-spreader"). I saw the exposed, beating heart, looking slightly bruised and larger than I would have guessed a human heart to be—in my eyes, huge. Although I knew at the time that I had a heart problem, fortunately I didn't have to have the transplant operation then because that was before the general introduction of cyclosporine, and heart transplants were heavily tilted in favor of fate.

Regardless, the movie remains one of my favorites, aside from its entertainment value, because I instantly empathized with the man in the picture, a theater, dance, and film director, not because I assumed any artistic relationship with him or came to see the person under that scalpel as me, but from the entire process the character went through: trying to overcome his heart weakness with bravado, thinking he could subdue his rebelling heart by pure determination, an inclination not to accept that he was as bad off as he actually was, the seizing of any little chance at "instant recovery," then the terrible truth of his fragility, both as medical patient and as mortal human, coming over and overcoming him. I have never known a heart surgery veteran who has seen the film who didn't feel somewhat the same way, even though the story line is completely removed from heart problems as such—the man could have been suffering from any life-threatening condition as far as applying the plot to yourself is concerned.

Reviewers said the script indicated the author was in love with death. That can be said since Death is a lovely female character in the film, but I see *All That Jazz* as a valuable parable: At the final crunch, you don't really want to embrace Death or have Death embrace you, regardless of how attractive Death seems to be. Most "heart wives" (including mine) turn their heads or leave the room when the surgical scenes start getting graphic (the way I did, as a boy, when kissing scenes came on the screen!). It may be that I go further in this than other heart transplantees, but even after many showings of the film (I bought a video recording) I get a spiritual and emotional tingle seeing it. I survived; I won. I defeated something not everyone defeats.

When I was discharged from St. Paul in mid-January, my pneumonia healed, I was in better bodily condition, but there was no longer any question as to wonted physical activities. They were nil. I had dropped nearly fifty pounds in less than six months, and my appetite was virtually nonexistent. Once home, the only things I could tolerate, though not truly enjoying them, were a few bites of French-dip sandwich or fried chicken. If that sounds shocking for a heart patient, remember, I was beyond having to diet because there was no way my heart could be "saved." That I was eating to stay alive was not the punch line from a fat person joke. My voice was noticeably weaker. I tried to do a little taping for an unfinished project at the university, and I just couldn't bring up the wind to make my wavering, cracking voice sound like anything but a centenarian's. Looking in the mirror at an unfamiliar, thin, and drawn face, I saw an old man whom I recognized only because he was in my bathroom.

One week's entries from Betty's journal during that time indicate the uncertain condition I lived in and the burden of support she labored under:

"Spent all afternoon making tortilla soup for A.C., and then when I brought it to him he couldn't eat a bite. . . . A.C. woke up feeling bad. Decided he did too much yesterday so he stayed in bed and slept a lot. . . . A.C. had a bad night but woke up about 10 A.M. . . . he took a shower which wore him out; already asleep looking very pale. . . . I fixed salmon croquettes and he managed to eat [some], even if it didn't taste good. . . . Today he's doing fairly well with eating, though everything has the taste of acid. . . . Ended the [week] with a trip to St. Paul emergency because A.C.'s heart rate was 100 and more, and he's been so short of breath."

Things got worse. Betty wrote, "A.C. couldn't sleep last night and

got up at 3:30 and tried to work. . . . He has had an uncomfortable
day because it is getting harder for him to breathe. . . . The cumula-
tive effect on me of watching A.C. becoming frailer and weaker is
really getting to me. . . . He's felt so bad today he hasn't even talked.
. . . Sometimes I think we may not make it." A family crisis involving
two of our children (brought on in part by the pressure of my
dissolving physical and emotional state) boiled over dramatically one
night into a screaming physical encounter, and she agonized: "Tonight was the most terrible night of my life."

The inability to sleep or rest grew while my condition worsened:
"Neither A.C. nor I could sleep till about 4 A.M. No reason. . . . It's
1 A.M. and A.C. is knocked out. Hope the same for me. . . . A.C.
didn't sleep till morning, [and] I had to make two runs with breakfast. The first time I couldn't wake him up. . . . This morning I found
A.C. asleep downstairs on one of the living room sofas. . . . A.C. had
his usual night—no sleep at all. . . . Story on transplant patients in
the N. Y. *Times* today. Depressing and a little scary. Some people
just die because they can't get a heart in time. God help us, please."

Winter deepened, and weekly calls to Houston drew only apolo-
getic admissions that there simply were no suitable donor hearts
available. The coordinating nurse at the Texas Heart Institute told
my wife, "The first thing someone asks every Monday, when the
committee meets, is, 'When are we getting Greene a heart?' "

My own good feeling, strong when I first returned home from the
three-week treatment for pneumonia, dwindled as the days passed.
Once I must have let some psychosomatic control take over because
one afternoon, after a terrible night and morning, I became convinced I had pneumonia again. As night approached I was edging
into panic or a near version of it, and my fears became genuine pains.
I couldn't breathe, something was binding my chest and my lungs.
Bill met Betty and me at St. Paul Emergency, and I received a quick
series of X-ray studies. Bill reported that I looked even better and
openly suggested my shortness of breath was psychological. I was
back home by 9:45 P.M. and the next day assured myself, in my
journal, "Feeling better, I guess from knowing I was not so sick."

Chapter 9

In April 1988 the University of Texas Southwestern/St. Paul Medical Center transplant program was announced, and at the suggestion of Dr. Kraus I had a wheelchair interview with Dr. W. Steves Ring, the surgeon who had been chosen to head the new Dallas center. He came from the transplant program at the University of Minnesota. He received a master's degree in medical science from Brown University, an M.D. from Harvard Medical School, a residency in general surgery from Duke University, and a fellowship in cardiothoracic surgery from the University of Minnesota. Asked in an interview what his best hour of the day was, he answered 7 to 8 A.M. Asked what his best asset was, he said a sense of humor. Asked what he was compulsive about, he said, "Caring for my patients."

I told Dr. Ring I was pleased with the Houston program, but after more than four months no heart had become available and I wasn't sure I could last till one was found. Bill Kraus assured me that if I decided to switch to the new Dallas program no Houston feelings would be hurt. After ascertaining that insurance coverage would follow me to the Dallas program—insurance *always* being a major consideration in any transplant decision—and that the testing done in Houston could be validated for Dallas use, by mid-May I had enrolled in the transplant program with Dr. Ring and his team, mainly because I felt a heart could be obtained quicker in Dallas, not to mention the difference in cost and convenience if the operation was performed "at home." Some of the Houston people, including Dr. Frazier, called to wish me speedy luck, and thanks to a change in national regulations, which formerly required a name be on only a single list, Houston kept me on its heart list, too. (Your position on a list, though, is relative, since even if you are number one, a suitable heart might not be found for you before one was found for numbers two, three, or twenty-three.)

Although the living recipient is ultimately the major figure in any heart transplant procedure, organs can't be obtained on some standardized automatic basis, so the donor is second in importance to the recipient. There are many prerequisites for organ donation, beginning with size, blood type, age, and the general state of health of the dead person.

Size is important; a new heart must be reasonably similar in size to the old heart and must have about the same pumping capacity (which is one reason few female hearts are transplanted to males), but in an emergency a slightly larger or, more likely (as in my case), a smaller than optimum heart can be used. (Transplanting from man to man or woman to woman is *homografting*, while male to female and vice versa is *heterografting*.) Too large a replacement heart is dangerous because it cannot function at full expansion capacity if it is too tightly packed into the chest cavity. Hearts, unlike livers, cannot be whittled down to size, or resectioned, the surgical term for it. The heart must fit within a cavity that is well defined by the structure of ribs and lungs. Liver "resecting" is chancy, but in emergency cases it is done. Reports from some surgeons indicated that by 1990 livers were being split and sections taken from living donors with growing frequency and success. Twenty-two-month-old Alyssa Smith of Texas became the first living-donor liver transplant recipient late in 1989 when Chicago surgeons used a section of her mother's liver to replace her congenitally defective one. This could be a partial solution to the organ shortage, greatly expanding the number of patients who can be given new livers from available donors.

Another process reported to be successful is the emergency procedure wherein a donor liver is inserted next to a failing organ when the patient is in a coma. Later the bad liver and the auxiliary one are removed and replaced by a single new liver. During a coma an auxiliary transplant is less risky because it involves less surgery.

Donor hearts must be viable, healthy organs from a healthy physical environment. This is another reason that organ donation is not as simple as having a request for organs granted. No use replacing a bad heart with a questionable heart, and on the other hand, no use wasting a good heart on a person who isn't going to survive the transplant. If you put a good heart in a bad body, no one benefits; the transplantee may die from other causes, and a qualified recipient may not survive because the good heart was not available.

The donor's blood type also should match the recipient's blood type. There are four major blood types: A, B, AB, and O. Blood types B and AB are rather rare. Persons needing organ transplants with these blood types sometimes wait longer for a donor. However, type O is called the universal blood type because it does not contain anti-A or anti-B antigens (which stimulate the production of antibodies that forge rejection); therefore, blood types A and B can, in an emergency, use an O heart, and AB can (in many cases) use A, B, AB, or O. But O, which was my blood type, can use *only* an O heart. There seem to be more O types than any other, but in nearly every case where a potential transplant patient waits an inordinate number of weeks or months for a donor organ, the patient will have O type blood. Despite what O type patients and families sometimes imagine, this waiting isn't often because the O type heart was deliberately assigned to another, rarer blood type. Type O's wait longer simply because there are so many of them. Transplant surgical teams do not often resort to cross-over organ use because it is unfair to us O types. After all, if you wait on a list for months, you are not likely to cheer at the news that an O heart that was potentially yours has been given to a B or AB blood type even though, if this happens, it is predominantly because the rarer type was near immediate death. (Blood type requirements also apply to liver, kidney, heart-lung, and pancreas organ transplants.)

Birth age is less important than physiological age, and as transplant technology advances, age boundaries for both donor and recipient are retreating. Thus, surgeons are constantly testing and expanding parameters of age. Depending on the size of the recipient, a donor can be between the ages of birth and forty-five years for livers, from ten to forty-five years for pancreas, heart, or heart-lung use (except for very young children), and between twelve months and fifty-five years to qualify for kidney donation. Depending on the condition of the material, there are no age limits for bone, tissue, and cornea donation.

Donors meeting blood type requirements and limits of age would not qualify if they had a history of disease or had suffered an injury involving donor organs. Organs will not be used if the donor suffered from diabetes, hypertension, most vascular (blood and lymph system) diseases, untreated fungal, bacterial, or viral infections, or malignancies (cancer) other than brain tumors. Heavy smokers would not qualify for heart or heart-lung transplantation, or alcohol or drug abusers for liver, kidney, and pancreas transplantations because the condition of their organs would be highly questionable.

AIDS screening tests are done on donors as standard procedure with any type of donation, organ, tissue, bone, or cornea, and as with other irreversible systemic infections, donors with the manifestations are not taken because there is no way to determine if an organ or the whole system is invaded by the virus or at what stage such symptoms may have become life-threatening. Overall, the ideal organ donor should have been, except for cause of death, in relatively good health.

One question some families are afraid to ask or feel is inappropriate, therefore hindering their agreeing to donate organs, concerns costs and expenses. As in most postmortem procedures requested by the institution, the donor family faces no expense from organ donation. Expenses incurred from evaluation and retrieval of the organs are assumed by the transplant agency, which collects from the recipient's insurance carrier or from Medicare. The donor family does pay for hospital costs prior to donation and for final disposition of the body.

The family has the legal right to say which organs will be donated as well as make stipulations regarding the race and geographical location or origin of the prospective recipient, though these stipulations are seldom enforced. However, it is illegal for anyone to receive payment for organ donations. (I personally feel there should be some kind of compensation, if only to repay the agony so often involved in making the donation decision. I think some form of tax relief could be instituted without exposing either donor family or recipient to embarrassment or publicity. There are reasonable arguments against even this, however. The potential pitfalls are numerous, such as families splitting up over who gets tax credit, a possibility of illicit identification of donor organs, and the many other greeds and connivances human frailty allows. Still, I believe some compromise could be reached that would greatly advance the donation process.)

Many states have a space on the driver's license for the holder to sign agreeing to personal organ donation, and most people believe if they sign it—or sign a donor card—their organs will be available automatically in case of their death. But no matter how legal these documents are or how strong the pronounced indications of the deceased might have been, no hospitals (at least none I have heard of) will go against family wishes in the matter of organ retrieval, and all will seek survivor approval for any sort of organ donation. There are religious and ethical considerations. Some religious groups oppose organ transplantation, and there is the foreseeable malpractice suit lurking on the fringes of any transaction not completely and legally accepted by the authorized survivors.

There have been shocking examples of backlash of donor generosity, including instances where defense lawyers argued their client did not murder a certain person (a brain-dead donor who had been mortally wounded by the defendant or hit by a criminally drunken driver), because the still-living victim was actually *killed* by the retrieval team doctors. That is why hospitals, in trying to protect themselves from such courtroom capers, seek formal consent from the next of kin and have their lawyers make certain that state brain-death laws are being interpreted correctly.

Even after giving permission to use organs, a family member can reverse himself or herself. There was an instance, in my experience, where this led to considerable complications at the waiting end of the process. A candidate had been informed a suitable heart would be available, and the retrieval team was preparing to fly to the out-of-state hospital, which was several hundred miles from Dallas, when the mother of the brain-dead donor could not face the thought of the donation and changed her mind. Nothing was done to try to persuade the mother otherwise, but back in Dallas, the would-be recipient, who was prepped for the operation but not opened, had to once again return to the crushing "normality" of waiting for a heart after those blissful hours when one seemed assured. (In this case a suitable heart was found within a short time, and the candidate's agony didn't have to be prolonged or repeated.)

My emphasis on the one case may sound out of proportion to its importance, but this is not an uncommon happening. (I am not referring to the refusal of families or individuals to donate organs, a rather frequent occurrence, but to donations that have already been committed and for which medical preparations are already under way.) Anyone who has lived through the tensest time in his or her life—waiting for delivery or death—can appreciate how disastrous such an unexpected delay may become. Had the person mentioned not gotten a suitable heart rather quickly—the rapidity strictly a fortuitous matter—there isn't any question but that her recovery would have been grossly impeded.

In 1968 the Uniform Anatomical Gift Act, since adopted by all states, named the following order of consent for organ donation: spouse, adult son or daughter, either parent, adult brother or sister, guardian, or any other authorized person. The U.A.G.A. rules offer the basis for what the medical world likes to call "encouraged voluntarism," which means that using its tested system of legal guides makes it possible for families to donate organs without feeling they are pioneering some new region or venturing into unknown legal and ethical territory. If donor families can be assured (gently and unobtrusively) that what they are being asked is asked of and agreed to by hundreds of other families each year, it becomes much easier to agree. At the time of donor agreement, some form of written or orally recorded consent is usually obtained, with witnesses. If certain family members are under sedation, in shock, or under the influence of alcohol or drugs, consent must wait until the next (by priority) authorized grantor is "alert and aware of the critical nature of the process." Sometimes this results in medical personnel having to relinquish hopes of a donation when family members remain unavailable for consent. Several countries, including France, Greece, Sweden, and Israel (with more added each year), have a "presumed consent" system, meaning a brain-dead patient is automatically an organ donor candidate unless objection has been made previously in writing. Although this system has added donor numbers, the increase didn't come as quickly as the medical community had projected. It took a few years for the law to assume the force and acceptance of custom. And even in countries with the law, strenuous objections or objections based on religious or social tradition will keep organ retrieval from taking place.

Different cultures view the dead human body differently. In some cultures the cremation of the dead is rigorously observed, and among certain American Indian tribes the dead are traditionally feared, not even talked about. As an aside, American translator Richard Lourie, in a *New York Times Book Review* article having nothing to do with heart transplantation, noted that Russians in their language "make considerable reference to *dusha,* the soul, where we (in English) appeal to the heart." This usage may affect both the way another culture might look on the heart transplant and how it might react to "presumed consent" laws: making the heart a less spiritual organ, therefore becoming less "sacred," through appreciation of "soul" rather than "heart" as core (from the Latin *cor,* "heart") of your being.

Several states in the United States have a limited "presumed consent" process applied by medical examiners and coroners for situations in which family members cannot be found, but this use (and opportunity) is rare. Although the laws might allow the use of organs if the deceased has no known kin or guardian, most hospitals would hesitate to take the organs for fear some provable kin or someone with guardian status might appear later.

The very success of heart transplantation since the introduction of cyclosporine has contributed to the severe shortage of donor hearts. A federal "routine inquiry" bill passed on October 1, 1987, orders all federally funded hospitals to adopt an organ procurement protocol, making it mandatory for the physician or a representative to ask survivors for permission to harvest valuable organs. The request may be denied if a family chooses. This sometimes creates its own barrier since a human heart, under present medical advancement, can survive for only a relatively brief time once removed from the donor, and a decision can be painful for family members who may be unable to make up their minds within so short a period.

Regardless of laws and personal views on the part of medical personnel (not to mention would-be recipients), there is a deep-lying prejudice against the donation of body parts that seems to be inherent in human existence. In fact, I would guess that almost every person has an unspoken resistance to the idea, and this resistance can't always be overcome. In 1989 a "Dear Abby" newspaper advice column carried a letter to that effect:

> Having read the letter in your column urging people to donate their organs after death, I am appalled by the piece. It was positively gruesome! The author was asking that his body be dismembered so that it is no longer a body—in order for others to live a fuller life. As many others do, I consider my body as the temple that God built to house my soul. It was not meant to be cut to pieces at death as if it were an old radio or some other nonliving structure. As far as I'm concerned, that letter was totally depressing.

Abigail Van Buren replied:

> I cannot believe that the God in whom *I* believe would object if a blind person were to regain his sight through a cornea transplant, or that a dying baby were to miraculously survive following a liver transplant. I am sorry that you found the letter depressing. Perhaps if someone you loved had had years added to his or her life due to an organ transplant, you would have a more tolerant view of donating organs after death.

An example of the mixed emotions possible on someone's part even after making the donation is found in a letter to the editor of *Dallas Life* magazine that had carried a story about my heart transplant. A Texas woman wrote:

> As a 45-year-old widow who has just been through the organ-donation process, I would like to address my comments to the media. There are frequent articles about patient recipients as

well as celebrity doctors, but no comment is ever made about the gut-wrenching decisions made alone when all hope is gone. It would have been easier not to make my husband's organs available. It was a tough decision made against the wishes of antagonistic relatives. It was time spent waiting in the hospital to sign forms when I would rather have been at home with my teenage children.

I'm not implying that I regret making the donations available. I begrudge [a transplantee] neither his new heart nor his new life. Nevertheless, a simple "thank you" would be in order, a thank you from both the media and the recipient. If my late husband's heart is alive and well . . . if some man is enjoying life, wife, and teenagers, we would like to know that our agony and our loss were not totally wasted.

I think most people should be able to see this woman's point: She has sacrificed a great deal, gone through an unusual kind of torment, and like all donor families that give organs, feels a certain amount of indecisiveness about the whole affair—and then, as she sees it, gets no recognition or thanks.

There are several problems involved, however. While some medical personnel may be so hurried and harried that they don't think about taking the time to make their own thanks evident, the sentiment is deeply felt nonetheless. Most members of hospital staffs who have the duties of asking for donor organs understand the tension and distress the moment is capable of bringing down on the survivors, and they appreciate both the gift and the often enormous pressures involved in making a once-in-a-lifetime decision on so immediate a basis.

Granting all the above things, the recipient seldom knows where his donor heart or other organs have come from and, therefore, whom to thank. Neither do the media. Most hospitals and organ banks will not reveal the source of organs without prior agreement on the part of both donor survivors and recipient; and most recipients I've talked to do not want to know, especially after the immediate wonder of the transplant has tapered off. For that matter, even the procurement teams often do not know the identity of the donor, though the health and vital indices of the donor have been studied.

And if you think about it, there are good reasons why donors are not identified and why recipients hesitate to try to find out even if it might be possible. For one thing (and these instances are certainly rare) there have been cases where donor families billed the recipient for the gift organ, even though federal law forbids the sale of body parts. But the moral suasion could be terrible: "Don't you think it was worth _____ thousand dollars to you to live?" Also, there have been cases where the donor families, not altogether by the recipient's desire, want to make the recipient a kind of member of the family. One heart transplantee tells of answering his doorbell to find a lovely young woman in tears standing at his door. She explained that he bore her late husband's heart and this was their wedding anniversary date, and she proceeded to put her head against the transplantee's chest and not only listened to his heart but spoke with love, assuring her late husband she would always love him, and so forth. It was quite nerve-racking, the transplantee reported, and in mind of future birthdays, holidays, and anniversaries, he would not agree to let the practice continue.

Of course backlash can work the other way: Suppose the donor organ eventually fails, and the recipient either dies or must be re-transplanted? Can't some lingering sense of failure hover over the entire episode if both donor family and recipient know what, when, where, and who? It seems to me, however, that the important idea is the recipient has not only been saved but has saved that core of another person.

What many people do not understand about the donor program is that the body is *not* being "left for science." It is not going to become a cadaver for medical school use; it is not being kept from the grave. And it is rank superstition to think that signing a donor card leads to an earlier demise. After organ retrieval the body is not going to look butchered. Procurement teams can assure donor families that consent will not interfere with funeral plans.

When internal organs are taken—and procurement teams try to "harvest" as many usable organs as possible from each donor—there is no evidence of the work other than the incision. (Most transplant programs speak of *harvesting* organs but not always in the presence of a donor family.) And even if eyes, skin, and bone are taken, the body will look natural through use of internal and external prosthetic devices. A greater problem comes when the body still appears to be alive but medically (and in some states legally) is brain-dead.

At the time of organ retrieval the body will be a living organism because, although brain-dead, there will still be the flicker of life as we define it in our own minds perhaps. Some may feel they are being forced to say good-bye to the loved one while the body is still sustaining life. The first reaction by the donor family, even families willing to give the loved one's organs, is often that of "you'll kill him before he has died"; they are unable to accept the idea that a body which appears to be breathing and living is, in reality, a corpse kept functioning through mechanical means. (This is not what is commonly referred to as a coma, where the continuation of brain activity is discernible by tests.)

The delicate question of what to call the brain-dead but still functioning body (not a corpse) has created at least two terms: *neomorts* (new dead) or respirated cadavers, and *biomorts* (biologically dead), neither living nor dead but dead for all hope of restoration. The term *brain-dead* has received acceptance as the description of a potential donor whose brain functions, by various tests, are nonexistent. The American Bar Association's definition is "irreversible cessation of total brain function."

If a brain-dead body does not continue functioning, the unremoved organs quickly lose their vitality and become useless for transplantation. But a still functioning brain-dead body can have a disquieting effect even on medical professionals, and many nurses and technicians prefer not to stay with such cases. A Texas nurse said, "I just couldn't take having to care for a body that was being kept alive but was already dead. I couldn't stand there and see the dead body breathing and looking as if it was simply sleeping. It was just too weird."

Mark Dowie, in his book *We Have a Donor* (about organ transplantation), tells of another problem that accompanies organ procurement. A California transplant coordinator, a veteran nurse, was asked to assist in a multiple-organ retrieval because the team was short one member. "It was a young girl, eleven or twelve," she told

Dowie. "Of course, during the [removal] operation you are not aware of such details because all you can see is an open body. Everything else is covered with surgical cloth. However, at one moment near the end of the operation, a little blond pigtail appeared from under the blue cloth." The nurse, a blond herself, said she was overcome with sadness. "I try to stay out of the OR as much as possible now."

The greater problem of organ procurement is not overcoming fears and emotions, it is actually putting into practice more of the urgency attached to donor response. It is estimated that about 2 percent of the people who die in hospitals each year are medically appropriate for organ donation, but even that relatively small percentage suggests that twenty to twenty-five thousand usable donor organs could be rescued. Under present circumstances, however, only about three thousand of these organs are actually harvested in any given year. Mandatory seat belt and motorcycle helmet laws have saved so many lives in motoring accidents that it has rather severely impacted organ donor programs nationally. Unfairly or not, among transplant teams, motorcycles are almost universally referred to as "donorcycles." Although no doctor would oppose the development of the air-bag for automobiles on that basis, this safety device, being installed in more and more vehicles, may create even tighter numerical limits on organ availability.

The shortage of hearts apparently will continue in the foreseeable future. It has also been estimated that as many as fifteen thousand people die in the United States annually who could be saved by a heart transplant. Another fifteen thousand victims of various severe heart problems could benefit from the operation, yet as of 1990, only one thousand six hundred or so hearts were harvested annually.

The average heart transplantee of recent times was a forty-three-year-old male and myocardial infarction was the most common condition leading to the transplant. Of those who underwent the operation, 73 percent were married, 90 percent were white, and after a year, 87.5 percent were living. That overwhelming percentage of white transplantees is not a matter of racial imbalance or discrimination. Although hearts have no racial description, there are small but significant differences between blacks and whites in the frequency of some lymphocyte antigens, which can occasion rejection. Despite the additional problems of rejection that might arise because of this, about 80 percent of all blacks who are transplanted receive kidneys (for example) from white donors. A mid-1980s survey conducted by Howard University found that blacks were less willing than whites to donate their own or their loved ones' organs. Ironically, the most common reason given was fear that whites would get the organs and blacks would be passed over. A noted black transplant surgeon is quoted as saying, "Blacks aren't donating. We're taking but not giving."

In transplantation the assigning of organs to the waiting candidates has created an ethical dilemma, and *triage,* a word originally from military combat use defined as "the assignment of degrees of urgency to wounds or illnesses in order to decide the order or suitability of treatment," is now used to describe the process of balancing all the factors of efficient use of organs, patients, personnel, and equipment. It also describes the duty of decision-making. There can be triage nurses or a triage team whose duty it is to say that this or that patient gets the newly available heart or liver or lung. (In military use it meant that under pressure of battlefield conditions the doctor or corpsman or whoever was in charge of the field facility had to decide quickly: "Save this one," "This one can survive . . . for now," or "Let this hopeless case die").

This problem of choice—who will get this heart and why—is ordinarily approached on two bases according to national transplant guidelines. The first consideration is the critical condition of the would-be transplant patient. To put it rather bluntly, the nearer death, the nearer a new heart—if a suitable heart is available. The second consideration involves the use of the donor heart itself. Hearts still cannot be transported very far due to their relatively short ischemic period. Coast-to-coast retrieval is out of the question at this time, so sometimes a donor heart has to be used on the next-worst case, usually based on how long someone has been waiting. To some extent the politics (if it could be called that) of regionalism applies; the nearer you are, the better your chances not only of getting a new heart but (as the doctors would see it) of benefiting from the postoperative regimen. Until organs can be freeze-dried or given some other usable preservation treatment, time is of the essence. The American

Council on Transplantation has given these periods for how long organs can be kept before transplant: heart, three to five hours; liver, ten to twelve hours; kidney, forty-eight hours; pancreas, eight to twenty-four hours; cornea, seven to ten *days*, and bone marrow, five *years*.

When the choice is made—as it must be, almost instantaneously—who makes it? Who assigns the heart or other organs? That varies with the transplant programs. Final selection is seldom made in the same way; sometimes it is made by a committee, sometimes one or two surgeons (especially if the lead surgeon is famous), sometimes by broader hospital policy. Usually it is made by the transplant team familiar with the candidate's medical history. There have been other limits of choice: how well the patient might comply with medication and procedures, whether or not the patient has other irreversible diseases, the prognosis of survival, and in some programs, the availability of family support. A few years back there was a great deal of scandal connected with one major transplant center when the program was accused of favoring rich foreign patients and the rich of our nation who were not only billed at higher rates but were able to contribute huge sums of money to associated institutions. (A Pittsburgh newspaper won a Pulitzer prize for its documented coverage of this practice, which the newspaper found taking place not only in its backyard but to some extent nationwide.)

The selection process is seldom made public, for obvious reasons. It would be too painful to know that your loved one was put second to someone else and therefore couldn't survive—no matter how badly the donor heart might have been needed by the one chosen. And since some transplant programs will accept riskier cases than others, there is no fixed set of guidelines to predict or time a transplantation. I am assured that today (in Dallas, at least) no one is turned down on the basis of money alone. I continue to hear of cases in which this appears to be happening, however, and weighing the enormous initial cost, I don't think I'm being too cynical to believe that the ability to pay becomes at least an outside consideration if two and two equals four in other aspects.

There are also individuals and families who may feel, though they may not express it that way, that the financial and spiritual costs aren't worth the gamble on a candidate's survival, although with more up-to-date testing and screening the gamble is usually mitigated or the candidate wouldn't have been accepted into a transplant program to begin with, especially a heart transplant candidate. Some programs, I am sure, have had to accept transplant candidates whose survival was questionable. This can be unfair not only to the candidates and their families but to all the waiting candidates whose risk factor climbs, facing the increasing dangers that delay entails.

This is the sort of thing that makes for rumors and inflammatory stories, but I do not believe it happens often enough to become a factor in transplant successes or numbers. You might ask: What about some ambitious surgeon who is eager to make a name for himself, selecting a candidate with extramedical value? Well, there is nothing to prevent favoritism or sensationalism within any ambitious heart, so what might be called "lo and behold!" hearts or livers or money can suddenly appear. And you don't have to spend a long life in these United States to have seen dozens of instances where tons of money and attention are showered on some individual because of heart-tugging circumstances or well-conceived media programming. Multimillionaires like to reach into their pockets suddenly and supply, often anonymously, the cost of such undertakings. The real shame is that only individual cases seem to extract this generosity; no one has yet set up a general heart transplant foundation for those who cannot conceivably raise the money.

Still, if the politics of wealth or influence enters into the procurement of a heart, I am happy to say I have discovered little (if any) of it. For instance, although St. Paul Medical Center is a Roman Catholic institution and many on the staff are members of that church, my endearing friend Father Jack Deeves, a well-known and liked Jesuit priest, had to wait seven months and ten days on a replacement heart, tying the waiting time record I had set for the St. Paul program. Not much recommendation for influence.

As a newspaper man of many years' practice I saw that the politics of wealth and influence entered into most things I investigated, from the running of churches to the naming of libraries, so undoubtedly it can have its medical moment. There have been cases where high-level intervention from Washington or another power center has gained organs or money for transplants, and there have been (and I'm sure will continue to be) nationally sensational organ availability cases, usually involving an attractive child, where publicity has swept aside other considerations.

There have been cases where certain candidates were reluctantly accepted for transplant when the surgeon would rather not have undertaken the operation; in such instances, you always wonder if some unseen pressure was applied, possibly from within the medical profession itself. In a case I heard about, transplantation was a failure on the predicted basis. On the other hand there have been a few cases where, to my knowledge, the hesitation of certain surgeons to risk their "safety record" led to the death of candidates for whom hearts had been denied because, they were told, specific hearts were either "not right for you" or weren't suitable hearts for any transplantation; then the rejected hearts were successfully transplanted in other candidates in other programs. One such case became a *cause célèbre* in Texas after *Texas Monthly* magazine reported on the story and wrapped the issue in a shockingly grotesque cover. You hesitate to take sides in such situations. When a candidate dies waiting for a suitable organ, one tends to think the surgeon was too cautious, but if the transplant is performed and the patient dies, you tend to blame the surgeon for being too zealous in pursuit of numbers.

Most of the media are quite defensive—too defensive—of doctors, especially famous ones working for famous institutions. Some stories concerning transplant programs at specific locations have gone overboard in awe of the directors of these programs and seem to question the validity of other programs. Local media will not always practice what might be called investigative reporting on medical programs that impact on the civic image or the local economy. Maybe it's understandable: The reporters and the editors walk the slippery tightrope of judgment, and even a medically trained observer finds it difficult to cast an unquestioned "yea" or "nay" vote on individual case problems—not to mention what the publisher might do if the stories put him in a bad light with the business community or the country club set. By 1990, however, there was no need to limit the usefulness of the transplantation process itself since it had been developed to such a point that any number of cities and institutions around the world, not only in the United States, could offer about the same amount of survival percentages as the more famous centers that from the 1970s to the mid-1980s had towered above the international field. And as for the historic "stars," a modern transplant surgeon can't get by with the arrogance found in a few of the 1960s and 1970s practitioners, even with a staff of worshipful automatons. Where success was once the province of an exclusive few, now it can be duplicated in dozens of places by surgeons unknown (or unborn) when experimental transplantation first began.

The truly difficult ethical/medical questions go beyond politics if not always beyond influence. Shall precious donor organs go to the one who is sickest or to the one with the best chance of recovery? Transplanting to an AIDS victim is apparently out of the question, although most transplant programs will not take the question and the answer that far when asked. Under present conditions it is easy to see why. AIDS is a deadly affair, generally terminal. There is no way to show that a transplanted organ might help that condition, and whatever condition it does help would be negated. In other words, uncharitable though the idea may be, why waste a precious organ on someone who is sure to die? If a dramatic new medication can be developed for AIDS, which research activity presently indicates not only could but probably will lead to a cure or some form of containment or remission, then the donor/transplant views involving AIDS victims will have to be rethought and remodeled.

Should the organs be apportioned on a first-come first-served basis? Isn't there a hard-nosed reality to giving a lifesaving organ to the patient with the most value to society (based on education, power, what)? And how about the waiting hopeful with the most dependents; or as is said to be true of sinking ships (an apt metaphor except for our day of ruthless self-servingness), should it be "women and children first"?

What about those who can pay? Some institutions, quoting costly loss experiences, refuse to perform a transplant unless the patient can show insurance coverage to handle the expensive operation or is able to put up a huge cash deposit. No question, this seems unfair, but it's a fact of modern reality, succinctly stated by an old axiom: Money makes the mare go. Therefore, faced with these questions, should all the eligible ones draw straws or toss dice? Of course to say that any one of the above should be the controlling factor not only violates human understanding but is impossible to implement with any constancy.

The would-be transplant patients I feel sorry for are those attempting to get the life-saving operation paid for through Medicaid or Medicare. Medicare in 1990 was denying payment for transplants done in any but a Medicare-approved hospital. The basis for approval was the number of transplants that have been done by the various centers and, to a degree, was a valid try at protecting patients from every institution that would attempt to get into the lucrative process without sufficient record to support its aims. In Texas the only city where transplants could be done under Medicare's coverage was Houston, at either Cooley's Texas Heart Institute or DeBakey's Methodist Hospital program. This meant the Medicare patient had to move to Houston to wait for a heart (which could be months) or at least had to live there for the operation and the minimum ninety days of recuperation. In a geographically large state these moves can cost thousands of nonmedical dollars, and most Medicare patients are trying to use that agency because of lack of money in the first place. In Texas as in other states, more and more transplant programs have proven their ability. Texas is such a big state that even cities as relatively close to Houston as Dallas and Fort Worth can be precarious places to be residing timewise when a donor heart turns up with its ischemic time frame of four hours or less. Houston is not centrally located.

What if the president of the United States needed a heart transplant? Who would dare tell him? Who would dare perform the operation? What would be the ethics of organ procurement? Surely somebody would know whose heart it was. And there would be a great outcry if any hint of favoritism were shown any ethnic group, including the so-called Anglos, yet what if the most suitable heart turned out to be from some donor who, when alive, had a public record of dissent, of crime, or some form of cultural or sexual deviation? And should the president be a woman or black or both, could a politically suitable (partisan/minority) heart be waited for? So perhaps the transplant process is not as fully realized as we believe it to be. Medically, yes; politically and ethically, maybe not.

Chapter 10

Once I was enrolled in the Dallas program, for the first three weeks my optimism bounced off the walls of the bedroom where I was ensconced. I hovered over the telephone expectantly, grabbing it each time it gave any indication it was about to buzz, and as fate (or something) seems to play such games, catching an inordinate series of wrong numbers—and if it wasn't a wrong number, it was five-year-light-bulb salespeople, one-room-free carpet cleaners, or aluminum siding agents, but nothing from the world of medicine and surgery.

June came creeping in, and everything about me was now creeping, including the spidery handwriting I can barely read in my journal. I was not bedridden and I resolved not to become helpless, but aside from taking myself to the bathroom, watching countless old movies on video, and reading, I seldom stirred from my swivel chair. Oh, for a while I assayed to move around somewhat, even getting out in the backyard one afternoon to try pruning a tree, but just a little of that and I gave up trying. More typical was this comment I made in my journal: "Felt bad—didn't do much but watch TV— didn't even read." I insisted on going downstairs to meet visitors instead of receiving guests in my bedroom, and there are fifteen steps on my stairway, as I well know, having counted them so often as I pulled back up one by one.

As the end of June loomed, I was almost past knowing or caring what day it was. On Sunday, June 26, I had a visit from Kate and Jim Lehrer (of the "MacNeil/Lehrer NewsHour," with which I had been associated), and Jim, who had bypass surgery a few years before, assured me he felt in his heart (!) I would hear something "this week." "Sure," I wheezed, "I'll hear something. Same thing I've *been* hearing—somebody telling me I may already have won the Empire State Building or earned a two-carat zircon tennis bracelet."

Kate shook her finger at me: "Oh, ye of little faith!"

Monday, June 27, 2 p.m., I was alone when I answered the phone. Dr. Ring said, "A.C., how are you doing?" and before I could do anything but grunt he was saying, "Well, listen. I think we may have found a heart for you. Surgery will be tonight. When can you comfortably get in?" I said thirty minutes would be stretching the time, if it made any difference.

Somehow (I was pretty excited) I dialed my wife's beeper, and when it digitalized our number, she said she knew what it was. She wrote, "I flew across the street to a grocery store, called home, and A.C. said, 'They're ready for us at the hospital,' and I flew home." My youngest son Eliot called just by chance and hurried to the house to answer the phones and house-sit while everyone went to the hospital. I got Meredith via beeper, and she said she would meet us there. (My other children, Geoffrey and Mark, lived out of town.) Within an hour Betty and I were in the car and on our way. I couldn't drive, of course, and by the time we got to the hospital I began fading out—in mind, if not physically.

Fortunately for my recall, Diane Reischel, a feature writer with the *Dallas News,* was interviewing Dr. Ring in his office when he received the call from the Southwest Organ Bank that an O type heart might be available. I view that period through a foggy pane of memory, so this adaptation of her story supplies a missing chapter in my journey toward salvation:

"In the next hour (after the quick phone call to Greene at home) Ring would consult with his transplant coordinator and the three surgeons assisting him later that night. He'd call home to cancel dinner plans. He'd have another Diet Coke, the usual sustenance of his twelve-to-twenty-hour days. And he'd study Greene's chart in preparation for the all-nighter ahead."

Dr. Ring is quoted as saying, "It's not really high pressure . . . I just enjoy [transplants]. There are few areas of medicine where you can really help someone, and this is one of them. I can go in and I can tell patients 90 percent of the time . . . that I'm going to make them better after I operate on them." (Fellow surgeons call Ring cool and "unflappable," and his former chief, Dr. John Najarian, of the University of Minnesota Hospital and Clinics, reported, "He's tough. He never seems to tire out.")

After I was admitted and installed in a hospital bed, Diane Reischel's description of me seems to mirror my semidazed condition: "A haggard face framed by strawlike hair, Greene lies flat in his bed, stares unblinkingly at Dr. Ring. In a few hours he'll have a new heart.

" 'We'll just take the old one out and put the new one in,' Ring tells him calmly.

" 'Like dropping a new motor in an old Ford,' Greene says, nodding. 'Well, I'm ready for a new motor.'

" 'And I'm ready,' Greene's wife Betty chimes in."

Meredith taped some of my reactions during those last few minutes, and on the cassette I sound normal enough, even capable of making sense above the noise of the hospital corridors. I suppose it was the knowledge I was finally getting a heart that gave me energy. I did not think of it as possibly meeting death but as gaining life. I know certain trepidations must have accompanied my brave chatter, but I cannot recall fear or regret during that preoperation period. I was quite unsentimental about those last hours of my dying heart, even if it had labored on my behalf for over sixty-four years: Get it out of me.

"You weren't scared at all, you were very eager," Meredith told me later. "You certainly hadn't shown this much energy in weeks and weeks. They warned you of all sorts of horrible things. Dr. Ring said, 'Now I want you to know, a lot of things can happen; you can have a stroke on the operating table.' "

My family was going through a time of emotional testing while I was being physically tested. "First thing, they [Dr. Ring and the transplant coordinator] told us that they couldn't be sure this was the right heart, but they thought it might work. They warned, 'Now don't get too excited. We won't know for a while whether it's a good heart. We have to actually look at the heart before we can be sure.'

"Roxanne Fall, the social worker, and the nurses stressed that warning; and we kept saying, 'Oh, but we don't care, we're just excited to be here for a heart, you know.' It was hard not to *believe* that it was a good heart because it was even harder to accept the idea that a transplant *wasn't* going to take place."

It was about 3:30 P.M. when they first came in to take tests. One by one, different doctors, different nurses, different technicians would thump and listen, take readings, draw a little blood or whatever was needed to fill endless numbers of glass vials. According to my daughter, the whole time I was just having a good old time, I was happy. "And you weren't being cynical or making wisecracks," she said rather proudly, since elderly cynicism tends to cause discomfort in the young. "You were just content. You had a lot of energy, but you weren't being a wiseguy at all. We kept thinking of people we should call while we waited. We should call so-and-so, or so-and-so would want to know. Then we were afraid that might lead people to think we were alarmed and afraid you wouldn't make it." I was in another world by this time, but Paul Duke, Jr., a friend of Meredith's, reminded everybody they hadn't eaten in hours when he came around about midnight bringing *fajitas*. Even some of the doctors partook. Since mine would be the first transplant under the new program, an unusual number of medical and hospital personnel were literally keeping in touch with the case.

At 10:24 P.M. in another operating room across the city, other surgeons had been performing a different kind of heart reconstruction; the body beneath their instruments was dead, but the heart they were extracting was living, beating, healthy: Plastic tubes from the heart-lung machine had been placed in the heart pipelines, the aorta and the vena cava, so that the life-preserving functions were maintained. Then a saline solution was poured over the organ and the aorta was closed, the pumping chambers of the heart were perfused with a substance that stopped their action yet acted as a preservative. Four main cuts and the heart was free of its first human environment. A nurse doused it in a basin containing a cold solution to wash away the donor's blood. The heart was then put into a plastic container immersed in an electrolyte compound that "fed" it during its stay out of the body. (This method of organ preservation is called core-cooling, whereby the organ is rapidly chilled with an infusion of a high-electrolyte liquid. Sometimes this is done by perfusion while the donor heart is still in the original body; more often it is done immediately on removal. The key, either way, is rapid cooling by replacing the donor's blood. Hearts do not need any other machinery during their journey to the potential new owner.)

Dr. Ring and the other U. T. Southwestern heart surgeons squeezed into someone's little Nissan and raced across Dallas to Methodist Hospital, in the Oak Cliff section of town. (The team that travels to obtain donor organs is called the *retrieval* or *procurement* team. The transplant surgeon may or may not be a part of the retrieval team.) Ring studied the history of its late owner, inspected the heart with his own eyes, and pronounced it good. Two other surgeons along with a nurse from the organ bank were scrunched into the small vehicle, but everyone was cheerful as they sped along heading for St. Paul Medical Center. The container with my donor heart was in a Styrofoam beer cooler, the kind you take to picnics and tailgate parties. After a seven-mile drive lasting ten minutes, the car swung into the emergency entrance parking lot, and Ring hurried with the cooler through that busy entrance, sending the heart on while he changed into new scrubs.

Meanwhile, the rest of the Greenes were waiting. "At 9:30 P.M. they started the operation," Meredith said, "and a priest came in and talked to us, a young guy, very nice. Wanted to know if he could help. They were all very cautious although I can understand why. But you'd waited so long and weathered all sorts of risks, and since the heart was there and this was the moment you'd been waiting for . . . we were all going to let ourselves feel excited. Dr. Kraus, who observed the operation, kept us posted on its progress either by telephoning the suite where we waited or coming out briefly to talk to us."

Dr. Ring says the heart transplant operation is not so difficult that any good surgeon couldn't do it because it involves only four incisions, but I'd like to make it plain that this is *his* view, not mine.

Ring later told me that when my old heart was removed, instead of continuing to beat for a while, as even a diseased heart will usually do, it collapsed with a sodden "poof!" I told him I realized I had only a matter of a very few months to live with it, and he said, "Better make that weeks." My heart was so enlarged, the surgeons were amazed that I not only had stayed alive but that the rotten heart had kept my other organs functioning. The operation was five and a half hours in length, but I was completely anesthetized throughout the procedure and felt no pain. And felt none from the incision itself. The scar, informally called a zipper or badge of honor, runs some eleven inches from my collar to the bottom of my rib cage. It appears, in some slightly different forms, on all open-heart surgery veterans, not just transplantees.

Betty and Meredith first saw me at 4 A.M. when I was still "out" from the anesthetics. "You really looked quite horrible," Meredith said. "You looked like a dead fish. Your eyes were completely yellow and glowing silver, and you looked like you were frozen on ice, which terrified Mom."

Betty's written account is graphic: "Ring and Bill [Kraus] came to the room to tell us it went well. We went in to ICU to see him. It nearly killed me. He looked as if he were made of yellow wax, and his blue eyes were wide open and unfocused. I thought, He can't possibly live, collapsed in a chair and cried. When we went back at 9:30 A.M., they let us see him again. He didn't look a bit better to me. Meredith and I went home to get cleaned up, but at noon the transplant coordinator called and said A.C. was bleeding and they were going to have to go back in to see why. They found two little 'bleeders' in a vein and sutured them. It took about an hour and a half. Dr. Ring came in and said things looked fine 'inside.' "

Meredith added, "Bill Kraus told us what happened, and Dr. Ring said this was pretty routine. Roxanne Fall became the liaison between us and the transplant staff. She took our mind off things. We could talk to her about it without becoming too medical."

During the operation I had an experience which I understand is not uncommon with patients who undergo anesthesia for long periods. I had two strong dreams, or hallucinations. In one I faced the certainty of death. I did not think of it as a hallucination but as the real thing. It was terrifying in its vividness. In the other I made a milder examination of death and its accompanying likelihood.

In that first dream I found myself locked in the Alamo—yes, *the* Alamo—after all the visitors and staff had left for the day. I opened a door, thinking it led to the outside perhaps, and found I could not reopen the door and was trapped within a sort of round stone silo that I recognized, to my horror, as a water storage tank which, when full, supplied the water pressure for the Alamo complex. And I realized that water was being automatically pumped in to fill the room to the top, and there was no way I could get out. I beat on the stone walls, but they were immovably solid. Yelling and shouting were useless, but I kept trying. My voice bounced back on me, carrying no farther than the walls around me. No one knew I was in that solid tank, and I knew I could never be heard, yell as I might.

As the water gradually rose, reaching my waist, then my chest, I realized that not only was I facing certain death but a strangling, choking kind of end. I began to set terms of acceptance: Should I struggle until the tank was full, cutting off all my oxygen, or should I make one huge gulping intake of water, thereby cutting short what would be lingering, panicky dying? In the dream/hallucination, I pondered all aspects of this problem, knowing that my time was down to minutes, then seconds. I crept close to death. I had not died but I felt death. Death felt like a stone wall: cold, confining, unscalable, dark, impervious, put together in such a way that there were no handholds, no protrusions that enabled you to climb, and yet it was not smooth, not slick and glossy. Death is impenetrable. Believe me, there in that sealed water tank I met death face-to-face. I did not have a feeling of panic. The problem presented was, could I come to terms with the knowledge that I was certain to die? That was the moral question that was being forced on me. Regrets of my life that perhaps I should have felt, I did not feel. Instead, the inevitability of that moment created a kind of relief: I was finally there. "We owe God a death. . . ." I had read Shakespeare's proposition many times before, but as I stood just before drowning, it returned to me as a comforting thought. "We owe God a death." Yes, payment was ready. Then as I resigned myself to dying, suddenly a 1936 Ford V-8 burst through the stone wall, letting the water gush out, and a crowd

of Baylor University drama students came cheering in, congratulat-
ing me on passing the test, which I realized this had been all along.
I was overcome by bewilderment and gratitude. Don't ask why a
1936 Ford V-8, which I never owned, or students from Baylor University in Waco, Texas, which I never attended and where I never
lived, and don't ask me how I knew my rescuers were Baylor drama
students. Remember, it was a hallucination.

(After I described my hallucinations in a Dallas magazine, I received a letter from Herbert H. Reynolds, president of Baylor University, who said he felt rather intimately touched by my experience
and thanked me for "dreaming" that my testing was done by Baylor
drama students when I had never attended his school; he also noted
that as a psychologist, he was quite interested in the hallucinatory
experience and, furthermore, he too had undergone open-heart surgery when he sustained a bypass operation.)

The second "dream" concerned a beautifully bound and illus-
trated book titled *Alphabets* by a Swedish author (my dream assumed I knew) and a world-famous calligrapher. The book was being
given by the hospital to several of us heart surgery couples during a
psychological exploration of death by the group. The book is so
perfectly remembered that I can still see the red-printed headings,
the light cream pages, the text in dark brown ink, and the distinctive
calligraphy, as well as photos and drawings used to illustrate the
applications of the various letters of the alphabet—including at least
two Swedish letterings not used by English, and I know virtually
nothing of Swedish except a few words I learned from collecting
postage stamps!

When I reappeared among the conscious, I was so convinced I had
undergone those dream states I told Dr. Ring (whom I addressed as
Dr. Ding!) that the test of my ability to face death was counterpro-
ductive. It scared hell out of me. Ring looked amused. "I don't know
what you're talking about, A.C. There was no 'test.' We got right
to work on you." Next I asked Betty to bring the beautiful book of
calligraphy the hospital had given us "when we were all sitting on
the floor in that sort of circular room, listening to that lecture on
heart surgery." "Book? The hospital didn't give us a book, or a
lecture either."

Betty remembered another episode: "Dr. Cochran, who spent the first twenty-four hours with A.C., told me at the end of the second day that today was the 'critical day' and A.C. had come through it fine. When I saw A.C. he had jerked the ventilator out of his throat. Dr. Cochran said it was probably involuntary but that they had planned to remove it anyway. With the ventilator out we could understand a little of what he said, and the first thing was, 'I want Paul Newman to play my part.'"

Are dreams dreams, or are they messages from the id, soul, psyche, or whatever that secret part of us wants to be called? There seems to be some motivation behind those anesthetically inspired dreams or hallucinations, some more-than-subconscious attempt to come to conclusions, to reach a decision, not about death but about life. Does one actually die at the apogee of anesthetized sleep? Does the body retain too ancient a memory of death to accommodate medically induced stillness and suppression that mimic death? Is death itself imprinted on our genes? No matter how austere we consider ourselves to be spiritually, I think there is a metaphysical mountain we must scale just to see if there is anything on the other side. I would not try to interpret these uncontrolled passages except that I have heard similar things from others who have been under anesthesia for long hours. One heart bypass patient told me he was pursued by a larger-than-human-sized bumble bee with a deadly stinger. He found himself running on two levels and attempted to escape the deadly pursuer by jumping from one level to the other, but the insect suddenly developed a stinger at each end of its body and did not have to turn around to kill its victim but could reverse its course and come zooming down either level. (An anesthesiologist later told me my dreams and hallucinations under anesthesia were not so uncommon, but my ability to remember them so vividly afterward was unusual.)

Immediately following my second opening, I was returned to the Intensive Care Unit where I was in a foggy state for some time. Meredith says I told her that my soul was flying about the room, threatening to leave; that for a couple of days it did this, and I finally got it back. She said, "You told me it was floating around, and you had to trap it to get it back. You said you trapped it by an act of will."

Whatever their meanings, these experiences remained with me and are with me yet, recognized but not understood.

After I left the confines of the ICU, or as my mind emerged from its long period of bewilderment, I knew I must find a way to bring back those hours when I was in the OR, hours I could not count on memory to relive. I began assembling facts and fancies that would help unfold the lost hours to me. It took more than a year, but eventually I could reconstruct the blank places.

Chapter 11

My recovery was remarkably quick and, as the medical world likes to put it, uneventful. My first physical triumph came after three days in ICU when I was allowed to come off the bedpan and use a potty chair. (I hope this isn't indelicate, but anyone who has been hospitalized for a serious illness can sympathize with my elation at the point.) St. Paul Medical Center was rearranging its surgical ICU at the time, and my room was behind a wide plate glass window, so that on the above-mentioned potty chair I could be observed by a host of visitors, staff, technicians, and so forth. But by that time I was so used to disrobing before various audiences that I could have performed nude in Neiman Marcus's Main Street window without a blush. However, in common with all the heart patients I have talked to, I didn't feel true recovery under way until after a week, when I was moved to a private room on the heart floor.

There is something about an Intensive Care Unit that seems to threaten those using it unless they are so completely out of things they don't know the difference. I'm not arguing for the change or rejection of ICUs. I know that the intense procedures can and do save lives, but for someone looking to feel better, more hopeful, the ICU soon becomes a prison, especially if one can overhear or observe the desperation measures being taken, often necessary under the extreme circumstances. Also, ICU personnel, while perhaps better trained and supposedly superior workers, cannot respond to their charges the way personnel on the floors can. ICU is a place of hurry! hurry! There's not much point in asking a patient "How are you doing?" since every little pulse and impulse is being monitored and recorded in a central observation place. I don't want to make too much of my emotions or sound ungrateful, but I think that a great many persons confined to ICU for various reasons think things are worse than they are and don't think they'll get out whole. Perhaps the reassurance that they really are going to feel better, in the majority of cases, might help some survive in better style.

From the time I arrived on the heart floor my recovery was (to me, at least) amazing. Ring had said the operation was easy to perform, but the transplantee's recovery and survival depend on patient and surgeon walking a tightrope of balanced medication afterward. That is where Dr. Ring and his team showed their skill. Thanks to the team's supervision and the enthusiastic group of nurses assigned to the heart surgery cases, I was on my feet eight days after surgery. I'll never forget how good it felt the first time I was allowed to shower, my third day on the heart floor. It wasn't just the process of getting all the surgical soap out of my hair or even the delicious feel, after so many days of bed baths, of warm water sliding down my body. What made it feel so good was the realization that I was able to do it. Yes, something as simple as taking a shower had been a monumental performance at the late stage of my waiting for a heart, and to be able to do it again and not have to be thinking, "How am I going to get out, get toweled, and get back to my chair?" was like discovering a bright new nation on the underside of an old, ordinary globe. I stood under the water for so long that the nurse who was supervising my recovery that day rapped on the bathroom door three different times asking, "Are you all right?" I came out, dried (and clothed!), and assured her that this shower had been worth a three-day supply of any form of therapy I had undergone.

In ICU, Dr. Ring had used an experimental bed with me, a bed that acted almost like a vacuum machine, sucking air through a built-in electronic filter to eliminate airborne germs, dust, or other minute particles, and supposedly balancing the mattress portion with air sacs that filled or emptied as the patient moved from one side to the other. Since visitors to ICU are obliged to wear face masks and disposable plastic gloves and gowns, there wasn't much work for the experimental bed to perform, and the automatic inflating feature let you sink far too deeply into its cushiony embrace; it was hot as the devil, even with air conditioning at speed—which is not always the case in a hospital. The bed, operating on battery power, also made a furious noise as I was rolled from ICU to the sixth (heart) floor. People stopped and stared, health professionals and visitors alike, as I came roaring along the halls, pushed by a rather nonplussed attendant who had never been near such a contrivance before. The young man pushing me shook his head continually, muttering to himself certain baleful phrases directed toward the bouncing, blowing appliance. Happily, Dr. Ring decided that out of ICU, the experiment wasn't worth the pain and discomfort it inflicted on me (not to mention having to put up with my howls of complaint), so he put me back in a regular bed and sent my puffing machine off to the limbo of the freight elevator loading area.

After that I survived what the nurse and I decided was a haunted bed—no fooling—which twice during one night rose mysteriously to its fullest height and, finally, couldn't be stopped or reversed by nurse or patient, forcing me to climb down via a chair (a tiny Indian attendant standing by pleading, "Pleece, do not fall!") and swap beds at 2 A.M.

My grasp of things strengthened, my misty conceptions began taking more identifiable form. I started finding myself. Something in me began to sing. Something sprang, not to new life but to *a* new life. It was more than a rejuvenation. It was more than a resurrection. It was a creation. Adam the second day in the garden: I was going to stay. There had been a period before the recognition of my desperation, even before I discovered I had heart trouble, when I was almost baffled as to what I had done, what I could do with my life. I had resisted "middle age" but could not come to terms with the future. I still clung to the goals that had motivated me from earlier years, but I was beginning to recognize that those goals were not only unattainable but weren't necessarily what I wanted on my horizon.

Now, recovering satisfactorily, I wanted to avoid that frustration. I needed to either set new goals or be contented with the short-range achievements of getting well, getting up, and regaining some of the physical abilities I had surrendered two or three years before.

On the other hand, I felt an obligation to my long-range survival. If it did complete itself so that I could launch new ships, new ideas of living, I wanted my boats and thoughts to be shared in some way more valuable to those around me than just the thought that I was lucky. I wanted to talk to a psychiatrist, a priest, an adviser of some kind. I had to get a new road map; I had to give myself something to fit the benefits, something to take advantage of this second chance, this second life. I felt obligated to so much: to my old self, to the donor (honoring an imaginary contract between him and me), to my new self, and to this second chance, not just at life but at living. I had to find some way through this joyful but confusing maze of emotion. I had to work it out my own way, but even the most intrepid explorer needs to consult a compass from time to time. This is where one's physician, in most cases, can take you only to a point; after that, you have to go alone. And I thought about it pretty much all day, those days of waiting. The thoughts were uplifting, I am glad to be able to say, not debilitating. There was a great deal of good feeling mixed in with my approaching this new future. And while I asked for and accepted all kinds of advice from several people, it was always my task, my deciding, that would control life. In the words of Captain Smollett, heard on an old recording of *Treasure Island* that my children played hundreds of times, "I've brought you this far . . . now the rest is up to you!"

A priest advised me, "Keep your hands off the steering wheel. Let God do the driving." For those of a religious inclination that's a very powerful, very useful piece of advice—*guidance,* more than advice. I put it in my spiritual computer, ready to pull it up for reference along with the medical requirements of recovery. And as far as changes and deviations go, it remains untouched.

In today's crowded, hurried medical center operation, where dozens, even hundreds of patients and would-be patients must be tended to or at least thought about, you become less than a number, and your bed is a prison. In the transplant patient's room, after ICU, there will usually be several rather large, intricate charts pinned to the wall, showing in minute numerical detail what responses and indications the body has given off. There are uneven lines under strange headings, none of which make sense to the uninformed observer, and at some point most heart transplant patients will sneak out of bed to have a look at these charts, only to be even more dismayed at the numbers under headings like: HGB, BUN, CR, NA, K, GLU, BILI, MG, AST CHOL TRIG, ALK/PHOS. Sometimes your doctor won't have time to explain the meaning and interpretation of these signs and symbols, and the nurses (since this is highly specialized) may not know.

There have been complaints from some transplant patients that whole herds of doctors and interns invade their rooms, scarcely glancing at them in the bed, undecided as to whether they are victims or heroines ("Hey . . . over here; I'm what you ought to be studying!"); but the medical entourage stares at the charts, which the patient can't make heads or tails of. And doctors can be dismaying, especially if the patient is unsure just how successful an operation might have been or if the future is, indeed, going to happen. It takes a lot of persuasion and downright sweet-talk to bring some people around in the face of uncertainty. The slightest hesitation on the part of a doctor can become instant booger-bear, the casual remark turned immediately into a prognosis of danger. And if someone frowns or glances over at you in bed with a questioning look in the eye, it can't keep from alarming you. What have they found? What did they discover? Why don't they tell *me?* Or when some white-coated individual does nod or speak, "Goo' morn," it almost seems delivered the same way you tell a pesty dog, "Down, boy." (Of course it may be that the personnel can't read the handwriting of whoever wrote out the chart, or maybe he thought he'd seen you somewhere before, perhaps at his uncle's ninety-fifth anniversary party.)

In other words, it's not always the jarring effects of bodily injury that a patient tends to feel most, it's neglect, having gone through what to him was a once-in-a-lifetime exposure to death, which to the medical staff may be a daily occurrence. If I were allowed to give one piece of advice to any medical professional working with very sick or terminal patients, I would say, shower just a little attention on them.

Not all day, not an hour at a time, but a little private, personal notice.
Make the patient *think* he or she is your target for today. Even if
you are feeling well or feeling great, you feel weller and greater with
the attention. This is one reason that, with the spread of successful
transplant programs today, my personal choice for entering a program would be at a smaller center, one doing fewer but still high-
quality transplants, not one of the world-famous hospitals where
uneventful or "ordinary" transplant operations are so routine that
the patient can become resentful from what is perceived as deliberate
disregard. There is also the follow-up period and its parameters of
time—a few months under some programs, a couple of years under
others, but it should be forever. The transplant veteran should never
feel deserted or overlooked or unwanted.

I used to joke about this prevailing feeling, in talking to recently
transplanted patients, advising them to have something distinctive
about themselves or their case. I was lucky, I explained tongue in
cheek, because by being the first adult heart transplant done in the
Southwestern/St. Paul program, my progress was watched closely,
and as I progressed the staff learned how brave and sincere I was, and
so I was given a lot of forthright information about myself that, to
some, could have become a burden of trepidation. I teased the
coronary care nurses, telling them they'd better see to it that I
survived or the whole show might go down the tubes. One night
nurse smiled and said, "Awesome!"

Because I was first, it was a matter of curiosity as well as medical
observation that my uprisings and downsittings were kept close track
of. Early each morning, once I was out of ICU, Dr. Ring would come
in my room and, while I shaved, discuss my condition, watching with
a surgeon's fascination as I maneuvered the hospital's single-use
disposable razor through its third or fourth shave without drawing
more than a milliliter of blood. I'm sure he was unable to pay such
attention to most of his subsequent transplant patients, but it sure
worked well for the first one.

I had anticipated spending three weeks in the hospital following
the heart transplant, but I was home in two. The U. T. Southwestern
Medical/St. Paul heart transplant program kept the next four transplantees only ten days in the hospital and later released some in as

few as six days. During my final days in the hospital, all my vital signs were good, my lab studies were excellent, my strength was returning—and I felt a decade or so younger. This was a benefit I hadn't really anticipated—the enormous wellspring of feeling good that came from suddenly having a new, working heart. My old heart had been dying so gradually over the years that I had forgotten what it was like to be energetic and alert physically, an exuberance that took only those few days after the operation to begin manifesting itself. And for a man, even one my age, *especially* one my age, to come along and have restored so *much* that he hadn't expected, even if he had not had a heart problem, it was miraculous. Even now I sometimes take a quick inventory of myself—health, vitality, looks, emotions, hopes, ambitions—and noting my high levels of satisfaction in each of the categories, I find it hard to get over, hard to grasp . . . the broad impact of restoration, the continuingly joyous outcome of it.

Chapter 12

In my enthusiasm for regained vigor, I may make recovery sound too miraculous, too effortless. It was successful according to the projections of the medical teams and well beyond what I had looked for, but it wasn't without hours of stress and doubt, those setbacks and sudden onsets of consternation. And it would be a disservice to those facing a similar situation to make it sound simple.

Neither I nor other transplant patients I have encountered came out of the operating room fog feeling heroic. Most of us, whether we like to remember it or not, went through long hours where our valor played second fiddle to fear. At first it amounts to "What do I do now? What else are they going to do to me?" Then comes a stage where assurances and best wishes have no meaning, perhaps even sound as if they might indicate the opposite: "Are they saying this to cover up the real situation?" "Does she (or he) expect me to believe that without any better evidence than 'You're looking great'?"

Not every transplantee makes it out of the OR, into ICU, and onto the cardiac floor with the same speed and exhilaration as others. And granting survival statistics of 85 or 90 percent, there are some who do not make it out of the OR or the ICU at all. Even in a highly successful program such as Southwestern Medical/St. Paul's, there have been wide variations of response and recovery, individuals whose emotional and physical well-being tracked quite differently from mine. Some of the heart transplantees, for example, have been irked by the return of old disabilities and symptoms, ailments and maladies that couldn't be cured or corrected by a new heart. Some have responded differently to medications; skin lesions appeared on the face and balding head of one of my friends, a female transplantee's scalp grew too sensitive to tinting so she had to cut her hair short and shampoo every day, the ankles and legs of others swell badly without the use of diuretics.

I certainly didn't escape unscathed. There was an immediate post-op period when I lost contact with myself. That's common enough under certain dire circumstances, but my recollection of that period makes it seem to me to be something from another age, a time warp from—which? past or future? I kept repeating aloud when I was alone: "Are you kin to yourself?" I was fascinated with the phrase, putting it to no particular use but ruminating: "Are you kin to yourself?"

There was another long segment of time when I found myself crying for no reason, although one seldom does anything for no reason. It just seems so when you try to look back and remember. So you fall back to using that fundamentals-of-psychology expression, "kinesthetic reaction," or motor memory, where (the example always given) you get tapped on the knee with that little rubber hammer and your knee jerks in spite of itself. Thus I found myself crying from some memory tap by some rubber hammer. I couldn't stop and couldn't control it, although again I was alone when assailed by these teary jags. Was I still kin to myself or did the new heart make me a stranger?

I picked up my tape recorder and whispered: "Death and life ring harsh or sweetly through the corridors of where we are. We never ask why a baby is born, we often ask why someone must die. There is a purpose for every life, for every hurt, for every wonder." There is no such thing as a short life. Life continues before and after and forever. The radiance of one candle is not lost in the glare of the noonday sun. Maybe everyone gets this inclination toward self-inspection (or human placement) in the throes of dubiosity, or was it (more likely) that compulsion to grandiose speculation about life that seems to motivate us as we think on, stare at, or look around, a profound situation? Although my emotions were not religious in any sense of an organized approach to my thinking, for a while in my room I sang hymns or mumbled them all night long; not exalted anthems but old gospel songs: "God will take care of you . . ." and "Leaning on the everlasting arms." It was like a passion, a tearful, trembling voice, myself a secondary, curious observer both performing and listening. This too came from something and wasn't without reason, but from what internal motivation? Was there any significance to the hymns I hummed? Kinesthetic reaction? (I had worked my way through college by singing on a radio gospel quartet, so the old hymns spring to my mind as easily as the Artie Shaw and Glenn Miller tunes of early years.)

Does this unguided introspection happen to every transplantee? I think it will or that it does. Maybe, as with me, the individual either doesn't recognize it at the time or considers it all a phase of the anesthetic: "I went a little crazy under the gas." More important is the recognition that it is almost bound to happen, and when it does it may very well seem to isolate the patient from the world, even a world of friends and kin. (At first my family thought I was making up all the "events" I described. "Aw, come on, Dad," one son finally had to say.) I would almost certify there will be a time when wives, sons, daughters, fathers, mothers, and friends will wonder, What's wrong with this guy?

I wasn't unhappy but I was dazed, not quite sure who or what I had become as of now—the eternal *now*. One night I woke briefly to record a dream: "Phantom bells ring in my head; phantom voices tell me stories that I don't know whether to believe." That soul my daughter said I spoke to her about, the one that flew around the room and had to be corraled by an act of pure will? The farther I get from the event, the stronger it becomes. At the time I told her I was sure I was recollecting the episode with clarity, but I soon lost it. Then, unbidden, it came back to me in a reverie of sorts, a second breaking out of a trance, the *deja vu* of a memory. On that return visit, my soul was indeed floating and flying, but it was trying to escape me; something (Someone?) was attempting to either abduct it or seduce it from my life. Had I been keeping my metaphysics warm all my life by merely crawling between dry ribs, as T. S. Eliot accuses "our lot"? And why not some otherworldly enticement, having lost or exchanged that innermost self, that secret other self we call heart . . . and soul.

My involuntary tears became identified as bafflement, baffling. Was I again bearing a traitorous heart or a good one? I never grew quarrelsome (I don't think; the nurses still loved me), and my frustration was more querulousness than anger or despair. I had determined to give up anger even as early as the second day out of ICU, especially anger at the public turn of events. There is a satisfaction I still have that I no longer get upset over the rocking of the boat, which is a true exercise in restraint for a longtime editorial columnist and commentator. Not that I became (or remain) apathetic, but with the first indication of a successful new heart, I resolved to grow more tolerant, more understanding, if not initially more forgiving. But wait, I told myself, how can you become more understanding and not forgive? You can't, so I determined to include forgiveness in my new system, but my determination faced (and faces) daily testing and doesn't always pass the test.

I tend to forgive anyone under the age of forty for minor trespasses and misdemeanors, and I'm sure if I make it into my eighties or nineties I will pull that piece of calendar thinking along with me, upping the cutoff number every decade or so. This same attitude seems to be aroused in the transplanted heart of any age: forgiveness. And forgiveness extends to casual lapses by the nurses and doctors. Take the cardiac biopsy; it is usually a reasonably short and only moderately painful operation, easily overcome (Band-Aid surgery, the jovial cath lab crew calls it), but some doctors who do the biopsy can be a little more punchy and pushy with the introducer and the catheter. And sometimes the invasion point on one's neck, instead of disappearing in a matter of hours, becomes garishly purple. But for heart transplantees—the ones I have been most exposed to—the whole thing becomes matter for a certain kind of bravado: "Man, is he [the doctor] a butcher!" However, if offered a choice ("Would you rather Dr. X do your biopsy, then?"), the veteran patient will smile and lift an eyebrow, as if to say, "Ha! . . . I can take it." In other words, we transplantees forgive easily. And why not, when we have discovered there is no otherwise?

With equal determination I abhor surprise. I want rocks of certitude as I step-stone my way across the unbridged streams. Few things surprise me, if that doesn't sound too smug, too elevated. Do all transplantees feel this way? I don't know; I can witness only my feelings, but as before, I suspect a good many have gone through the same sort of determinism and remain as I do.

Everyone's approach to safety is different, but especially when danger is seen as momentary. Momentary danger can be invigorating, whether experienced as the driver of a race car averaging 240 miles an hour or as a youngster riding the roller coaster at an amusement park. But blind, uncontrollable danger, danger that doesn't let you count the laps, that won't let the roller coaster ride end, creates depression and hopelessness, which combine into grim and hateful unhappiness. Unhappiness, like fear, can take over your life, can make you ill or keep you ill according to the strength of your belief in danger. If, like the professional racer, you know that your machine (your body) is capable of certain gains and you believe them achievable, then it is a temporary thing. But if on the first ride on the roller coaster you confuse it with ultimate disaster, then it not only limits but inhibits recovery—of body and, more important, of spirit.

There are many names for it, and just about everyone coming out of the darkness of physical despair knows a season of it: postoperative depression, aftereffects, letdown. In the case of heart surgery it has become known as the "cardiac blues." While it seems to affect bypass and heart-valve replacement patients more frequently than transplant patients, it can overtake even the most optimistic and enthusiastic recovery process. This unhappiness can begin in the Intensive Care Unit where the very procedures that make the unit so valuable tend to isolate and exile the patient in his or her own mind. Nurses and technicians seem always in a hurry, throwing you a smile as they scoot by your bed or cubicle, or sometimes in an emergency, not even that.

I wouldn't want to leave the impression, however, that cardiac blues is something a strong person can avoid or that it afflicts only weaklings. To some degree it hits everybody, especially in those 3

A.M.s of the soul that Mr. Francis Sinatra sang about, when you can't sleep or have just returned from the bathroom after your third or fourth trip since 11 P.M. And you can't keep from asking yourself if it's going to be this way the rest of your life—without daring to further question about how long *the rest* may amount to. But again, with the resurgence of new life and the renewal of what poet Dylan Thomas calls "the force that drives the green fuse through the flower," such misgivings and confusions drop away or clear for most patients, and by the time they have gotten back into some accustomed ritual, those frustrations and inexplicable periods will have faded even if the patients are still doing that Lasix-inspired bathroom journey an inordinate number of times.

I found myself wondering about myself; I found myself wanting to know not just surface or casual reassurance but evidence, something I could lay my hands on, so to speak—something beyond merely "feeling better." Did I really feel good, or was this just the other side of the terrible coin I had paid in the months before? This feeling toward feelings, while not always prevalent, certainly refused to disappear. I could not proceed through a process of belief alone. I had no evidence to base belief on other than the interior evidence of mind and feelings, nothing on which to base a medical decision, and few things on which to base life decisions—a certain determination but not brave determination. A certain hope and certain expectations, but neither wildly nor extravagantly possessed, certainly nothing that could relieve the anxiety of fear that I suppose everyone is burdened with when approaching or departing a major medical experience.

Did I find a solution? I find one now, but did I find one then? I found some kind of solution. I survived. That in itself becomes a solution, like a road map discovered after you've reached your goal; it is still interesting to see where you went, why you had to detour, where you missed the chance to go straight through to a place or go around the difficulty of a barrier, a barricade, or a city. And it was months before I could look myself in the mirror and say, happily and believably, "All of you is better!"

I am not a suddenly reconstructed person; I have not had the years given back to me. I have only rescued certain things—abilities, capacities—but it took me several months to recognize the true force of this fact.

When I first returned home from the hospital I was seventy pounds less than a year or so before. I looked like a concentration camp survivor. Much more than having to recover from the operation, my body had to overcome the months it had declined while awaiting a new heart.

I had to sleep on my back for nearly two months following the operation. I couldn't sleep on my stomach because of my chest, and sleeping on my side, or trying to, seemed to squeeze and threatened to suffocate me. It was not the pain of the incision—my "zipper" has never been a problem beyond being ugly—but something more internal, as emotional as physical, I suspect. Why do I say that? Well, I have always been both a light sleeper and a sleeper who sticks strictly to his side of the bed and scarcely wrinkles the sheets. Emotionally, I am used to positioning myself a certain way, halfway between fully on the stomach and partially turned on a shoulder. When I couldn't do this, my muscles and nerve endings, which were so accustomed to being pulled or twisted in specific ways, couldn't "get with" my new full-on-back nocturnal needs. My mouth and nose became dry, my head developed funny pains, and my neck crackled like a pecan-shelling plant when I first arose. I think becoming able to sleep on my side, to turn my head back and forth in tune with a deviated nasal septum, to flop into a semi-stomach pose was a deliverance almost as refreshing as leaving the hospital.

I couldn't drive a car for a month after the transplant operation because of the strain that might be put on the incision site, but I began cardiac rehabilitation at the St. Paul Health Institute facilities within three weeks of the operation. Of course I had to adjust to a new internal rhythm. In time, under normal aging, you get used to having certain bones and joints aching with exercise, or you feel that your gait needn't be affected since your heart problem did not involve your lower extremities. All this may be true, but that "new start" business can take some getting used to. I had always considered myself a robust pillar of walking; many years ago I easily handled President John F. Kennedy's faddish suggested pace of "fifty miles in a day." Remember how he had his Ivy League staffers nearly killing themselves trying to do it? (Can we blame the jogging craze on JFK?)

When he first began the cardiac rehabilitation program, this upright pillar found he was shuffling, wasn't lifting his feet, *couldn't* lift his feet. He wasn't *able* to *not* shuffle. This persisted for at least six weeks, with my trying valiantly to control my feet, but they continued to flop-flop (in my ultrasensitive consideration). I mentally gripped myself and instructed my legs and feet: "Walk straight, damn you!" but the control I had exercised so well for so many years just wasn't there. I fussed and fretted to myself and was embarrassed that someone else on the track would notice my flop-flop gait. Like a drunk told to walk a straight line, I worked so hard at covering it up that it showed more and more. About the time I was ready to tearfully admit I was to be cursed with an old man's gait, I realized it wasn't something I must try to master by an act of will (for which I am famous within the family circle) but something that would correct itself as I regained normality. And such proved the case. Gradually I overcame the flop-flops, until in ninety days I didn't feel the unmanageable reaction when I walked. I soon learned also that every transplantee feels that flop-flop way about his gait those first few weeks of cardiac rehabilitation. My age and experiences in living helped me to accept such post-op disabilities.

Over a period, a new heart will usually conform to the size of its new enclosure, but it takes time and there are certain unusual "symptoms" that can upset and perplex the medical observer who does not understand this accommodation: The heartbeat is faster, and "wake-up" time for the heart at work is often alarmingly slow. Some transplantees, even after a year, feel a dizziness when first getting up from a long or fairly long period in a seat and will have to rest after taking a dozen or so steps before going on. While this can be a sign of more threatening problems, more often it is just the new heart trying to do the work the rest of the body demands and being temporarily unable to do it, probably resulting from the autonomic nervous system around the heart not functioning—the nerves having been cut and medical science not yet able to reattach such items—and the brain having to alert the heart to its immediate job.

My rehabilitation workouts initially consisted of moderately paced walking around the indoor track, seventeen laps equalling a mile. I made four laps the first day, but in three more weeks I was allowed to go at any pace with which I felt comfortable and could use the stationary bicycles. Because I was the first transplantee the cardiac rehabilitation staffers had worked with, my blood pressures and pulse rates alarmed them. Even after resting as much as fifteen minutes following exercise, my heart rate would measure from 102 to 108 beats per minute. Dr. Ring had to assure Nancy McNally, the beautiful, spunky Irish R.N. who supervised my Institute rehab program, that transplanted hearts did things like that sometimes for a year or more in their attempt to adapt, in size and rhythm, to their new physical environment. Short of his attempting to jog or run early on, turn him loose, Ring advised. Although it seemed to go against her Notre Dame training, Nurse Nancy turned me loose, but months later, with other transplantees in the program, she was still keeping a questioning eye on those elevated electronic cardiac readouts.

After ninety days, the most dangerous post-op period for a coronary transplant, I was allowed to begin work on the special body-building machines: legs, hips, torso, chest, biceps, triceps, abdominal, back—using terms and muscles I hadn't used since calisthenics days in the Marine Corps. The purpose of cardiac rehabilitation, for most patients, is not to put on muscle or chunk-up old or young bodies into muscle-beach contestants; it's to establish a rescue program for the heart and its functions, to enhance those functions, to make the heart operate best, whether transplanted, bypassed, revalved, or just sagging under its load. Certain physical routines can make a heart transplant candidate's condition better in some cases, though not curing or eliminating the basic problem, so that his stay on the waiting list is enhanced and extended. This is not necessarily a purely delaying action; it can help the candidate receive a suitable heart because in most cases his other organs have gained something from the beneficial actions on the heart, even if the coronary organ is not reestablishing itself.

In working out, I plateaued (as the body builders say); that is, I reached the level of weights and repetitions (number of times) on the various machines that I wanted to be able to continue doing to keep me in the best maintenance possible. Although I knew I needn't go on forever with certain of the higher-impact machines, I could continue to develop muscular tone and maintain flexibility. Of course, briskly walking for two or three miles ultimately became my every-three-days exercise of choice, but who knows? The vigor machines haven't nubbed me down yet. On the other hand, the older trans-plantee must quit comparing himself with charts, test results, and responses that are gauged for "other people," especially younger men. The competitive edge doesn't matter. It is not only unimpor-tant, it shouldn't exist because it emotionally burdens some males, especially formerly swift, powerful athletes who find it hard to accept that at their older age they are no longer able to play guard for the Bears or power forward for the Lakers. At first the male in me tried to entice the more civilized me into competing in the matter of weights and "reps," but thanks to age, experience, and accumulated wisdom—good things that sixty-plus years can teach you if you let them—I quickly cut that out.

The heart transplantee of any age is seldom striving to be a body builder. (I couldn't afford the body oil even if I could regain the body.) I am sometimes amused at (but guilty of) the competitiveness of some men who work out at the St. Paul Health Institute facilities at the same time as us cardiac rehabs. One young doctor (who didn't know I was a heart transplantee) approached me on a certain ma-chine, asking "how much" I was doing. I choked back an inflated figure (lying is unbecoming in one my age) and told the truth, that I was doing fifteen reps at 125 pounds. He looked pleased and informed me, "I'm doing fifty at 250." I didn't want to get into a contest, but a man my age, when having to fight out of his weight class, is entitled to whatever defenses he feels capable of getting away with.

"How old are you?" I asked gently but patronizingly. "Almost forty-two," the younger man said, hesitating enough so that I sus-pected he was actually implying an additional year at least. "Well," I said, squelching proud tones of haughtiness but experiencing for the only time in years genuine satisfaction in being older—"I'm sixty-five!"

In my first happy weeks of recovery I made some common mis-takes. My eyes took about six months to show what they were doing under the heavy medication. I changed my visual prescription, and it didn't work. I had been warned in the cardiac transplant literature about doing it, but feeling superior again, I got a new prescription too quickly. I discovered I could do close work better with a prescription that was twenty-two years old. I ended up with six pairs of glasses, including three of the close-up or reading type, which I keep stashed around the house at intermittent reading or working stations. My experience seems to be repeated among quite a few of the transplantees who customarily wear lenses. Contact lenses, which I do not wear, seem to work better than spectacles—or do I have it backwards? At any rate, one can anticipate a certain amount of problems with the eyes after a heart transplant and, presumably, other forms of transplantation that require heavy medication.

Another mistake was buying clothing too quickly after the operation. Unless you are prepared to buy *another* new wardrobe and have your glasses changed *again,* the heart transplantee must give time its due and wait to see where the scales will settle. Some of us now keep three wardrobes on hand: too small, it fits, and too big. I went from a 38–40 in the waist to a 32–33. I bought clothes at that size, knowing it couldn't last (shouldn't last; I looked skeletal), and have several pairs of pants I probably never will be able to wear again; but I bought cheap and will hang on to them in blessed memory, if for no other reason. Also, you can gain weight before you know it, and before you can stop. Gaining weight, for those millions of us who fight that particular fight, is so easy it overcomes us before we can catch up with it. And a new heart doesn't change things. It doesn't forgive anything but itself. I've known heart transplantees who let themselves get *quite* overweight, particularly around the belly in the case of men. I had a certain problem with "prednisone pones"—fatty deposits that appear on face, neck, shoulders, and hips where you don't need fat—above the belt, which fortunately was at the rear and didn't disfigure me (or am I fooling myself?). Without a heroic amount of dietary precaution from the calorie point of view, weight can be picked up quickly. Like everyone else, I had the "cyclosporine shakes" for several weeks following the transplant operation. These are barely felt tremors that make the hands tremble and (more annoying to me) the teeth chatter when first going to sleep—not the lively chattering of a chill but an annoyingly subtle quiver of teeth-to-teeth.

Because of the usually joyous state that the new transplantee goes through with a new heart, it becomes easy to forget that the body continues not to use in sufficient numbers overabundant calories. The medications, particularly prednisone, give one a fierce appetite. Although prednisone is *not* the anabolic steroid that some athletes have been found taking for bulk, the overall effect of steroids is to "bulk up" the body, even on women, and the transplantee discovers his bulk can balloon considerably if he doesn't work hard to counteract it.

And in that area, a heart transplantee's dietary problems aren't too different from those of the ordinary citizen who is losing weight or watching his diet. On my own I voluntarily embraced the "heart-healthy" diet: low fat, low cholesterol, low calorie, low salt, and no alcohol in any form. You won't find me trying to discover "legal" ways to slide under the turnstile; I stick as strictly as possible to whatever is prescribed, whether food, medicine, or activity. The nutritionists say we Americans eat too much salt with our too-many calories and fat-heavy meals. Salt is in practically everything canned, packaged, frozen, or fried. After determining how much sodium is the recommended daily allowable, look on the labels of foods you might think wholly innocent and notice the shocking amount of sodium in the contents.

The key is "low" not "no." Low can mean many different things but not always the lowest. Not to make life sound too grim, today it is possible to find virtually anything specially prepared in a low way. Although told it doesn't make much difference dietetically speaking, the diet soft drink, offering fewer calories and less (or no) sugar, has become a standard item of daily American life, and heart transplantees, like all other dieters, can (and do) feel especially virtuous keeping only diet drinks in the family fridge.

The hospital nutritionists told me something interesting. I had always assumed that salt was the one craving the human could never overcome or outlive, but I was wrong. It's the sweet craving that sticks with us from birth. It isn't a learned taste; babies love it. So in my unnatural greed for ice cream, I suppose I'm only human . . . or only immature?

Chapter 13

Until science comes up with new medications or processes—which is happening as this is written—I will be taking daily doses of cyclosporine and other immunosuppressants. Because our immune systems are deliberately suppressed, we transplantees are open to all kinds of illnesses carried by germs other bodies are able to throw off, so we must use antibiotics daily.

Some heart transplant patients reportedly resent the overly cautious advice of the doctors and nurses as the patient prepares to reenter the world. Since transplant patients tend to be grouped together in the minds of various members of the transplant team, all are warned about such things as being in the sun without sun block, even on an overcast day ("You're ten times as liable to develop skin cancer as the average individual"); catching a cold that might rapidly cause grave danger because the immune system is so suppressed. (I cut short a California vacation by ten days one winter when I suddenly started coughing and sniffling—I flew back to Dallas for X rays for fear a cold might rapidly turn into pneumonia. Luckily it didn't, but I would take the same precaution again if I caught a cold.) We are also warned about cutting ourselves, because blood thinners are prescribed that can cause dangerous bleeding, and developing diabetes or liver problems from the powerful medications, especially in the early, crucial months. However, none of these are inevitable or universal, and sometimes not even one overtakes the patient. After the ninety-day safety zone is reached and certainly after a year, you can forget how vulnerable you remain. But, many months after my operation, I still protect myself in certain ways: I still wear cotton gloves for driving and protect my hands from the sun's rays (thin cotton, as even specially made driving gloves of leather or nylon are too hot for use in Texas); I wear my wide-brimmed hat if I have to leave the car for lengthy periods (and carry a hat and a pair of gloves in the car); and I put on my fifteen-plus sun block when I swim or anticipate having to be in direct sunlight for more than a few minutes. Also, I wear long-sleeved shirts with the cuffs buttoned when I go outdoors so that even that inch or so between the cuff and the back of my hand is not exposed. I have no problem at all in obeying those restrictions. In addition to skin dangers of the medications, I have been sun- and heat-sensitive all my life. I've never been a sun worshiper or a deliberate tanner. As a boy I had to work outdoors many summers, and I burned and peeled, never tanned. My nose, chin, and forehead looked as though I'd developed a loathsome skin affliction.

I'll never forget one summer, early in World War II, when magnificent wages were being offered for construction workers on an Army camp near my hometown: forty cents per hour, regular; double time on Saturdays and Sundays! Believe me, those were enviable sums for that day for my level of skill. I tried to avoid the consequences of the sun's rays by wearing an old, hot (black!) felt hat and borrowed suntan lotion, which I later discovered helped cook rather than protect skin like mine. That season was not only among the hottest on Weather Bureau records, the heavens almost never opened, and when there was a slight crack, seldom did it spit more than a few miserable drops of rain from month to month. The hat didn't cover the back of my neck, resulting in a curious crescent of carrot-colored hair that drew unadmiring glances since this was long before the day of the "mohawk" haircut or postmodern punk. I was at the age where you dated every night, if possible, and I still marvel (after more than four decades) at the generosity one winsome girl showed by going steady with me that terrible West Texas summer.

Personally, the backs of my hands are as big a problem as any. The medications that transplantees must take can cause purple and red spots on the backs of hands, forearms, and other places if one's body receives a bump or pinch. On the backs of the hands, sometimes a blow so slight as not to be felt will cause blood to flow. Some of this thin-skin spottiness can be blamed on my age, I am sure, but much of it comes from the medication, particularly prednisone, that villainous steroid which we transplantees pray someday can be replaced in the transplant protocol.

Medication, especially cyclosporine, must be taken at the same times each day because it has a rather rapid half-life that limits its continued effectiveness to approximately a twelve-hour span, the dosages individually balanced according to periodic laboratory test findings. As noted, with cyclosporine and prednisone, serious side effects can occur with liver and kidneys. But thank heavens "prednisone pones" generally disappear as the prednisone dosage decreases.

Medicinally induced diabetes is always a danger with the powerful suppressants that heart transplantees must take. I had a flare-up of diabetes about three months after my transplant. Blood glucose readings were being sustained well above the 200 mark. But with a medium drug dose each day and a great deal closer reading of labels on food containers, and cutting down on my sherbet consumption (I had gotten the idea that sherbet could be consumed at will), I managed to reduce that blood sugar count to normal range (70–120) and hold it, eventually dropping the medication without ever having to use insulin. (Diabetics and others associated with the disability will understand that medicinally induced diabetes is what is known as Type One or noninsulin kind and is not necessarily permanent.)

Long after passing the generally accepted post-op danger points, I had had no rejection event. One member of the original Ring transplant group had to have a gallbladder operation fewer than sixty days after his heart transplant, but this was not a consequence of the transplantation and proved not to hinder his cardiac recovery.

Hearts have no gender and no race, so despite jokes and innuendos, there are no known physical, emotional, or character traits passed from donor to recipient. The heart is merely a muscle. Billy Williams was the only one in my original transplant group who knew whose heart he had—he wasn't as anesthetized as was thought when someone in the operating room mentioned it—an eighteen-year-old Texas athlete whose mother eventually visited Billy. Although I will always be grateful to my donor family that they allowed his good heart (because of my size I assume it was a male) to become mine, I do not want to know much more. A part of him still lives and I am alive, and for me that is sufficient. I realize that even with a new, younger heart, I must avoid the dangers that face any heart. I must not sink into complacency. This heart *will* remain-protected.

When I first considered having a heart transplant, I was warned that there was an informal "rejection factor" scale which, through experience, had been set at approximately 1 to 10, based on certain rejection symptoms common to most patients. A factor of 1 to 3, or possibly 4, was considered almost normal, nothing to rush you back to the hospital, once released. A fair number of patients did have to return, with rejection factors of 6, 7, or 8. A rejection factor of 10 was life-threatening, but while at the Texas Heart Institute in Houston I was told of a woman who had recently survived a recordbreaking factor of 15. She was retransplanted, and at the time I did not realize one could be retransplanted.

I thought I was demanding the impossible of myself when I vowed I would *not* have a rejection event. It was a vow based on nothing but determination. I simply declared to myself that I would not be satisfied with a three or four or even a one or two; I would go for zero in what might be an impossible attempt. And at the time it really was deemed almost impossible. Every heart transplant program warned that a rejection event (or "episode") could *certainly* be anticipated within the first few weeks after receiving the heart. It was stated as a virtual inevitability. If I didn't have a rejection event, the credit goes to the postoperative medicinal program in addition to the operation itself. So much had been learned from experience that through our weekly, biweekly, and monthly tests, lab workups and biopsies, only one in U. T. Southwestern/St. Paul program's first-year adult transplant crop produced enough rejection episodes to have to return to the hospital, and he was out and back to rehabilitation in a short time.

But there are always dangers of rejection, even as late as five years after what has appeared to be a successful transplant. I met one forty-two-year-old man who, despite five years with a successfully transplanted heart, was waiting to receive a second transplant. He insisted he had stayed close to protocol with medication and diet— he hadn't gone back to using tobacco, had stayed off salt, fats, and high cholesterols, and had exercised—but there he was, suddenly having such severe rejection events that a new heart was required. It didn't scare me but, approaching a year myself at the time, it gave me pause.

So can a transplantee ever feel like "I'm over it!" the way one overcomes a cold or the flu? No, not under present medical parameters. As in the case of the man referred to, there can be this puzzling condition that some few transplantees develop, chronic vascular rejection, that forces them to be retransplanted. Doctors aren't sure whether this condition is a more rapid development of atherosclerosis of the coronary arteries—deposits of fatty substances clinging to the arterial walls—or the result of powerful rejection reactions caused by the individual body. And the transplantee can't experiment to find out.

The original U. T. Southwestern Medical/St. Paul adult heart transplant group numbered five. Within two months, in addition to me, Dr. Ring had done Billy Williams, Wayne Bavol, Robert Morgan, and Jerry Moser. In the hospital and at gatherings we were a regional curiosity: Some of the group had caps and T-shirts made (red lettering!) proclaiming their position in Ring's transplant sequence: "SW/St. Paul Med Heart Transplant #3." We initially met twice a week for lab studies and clinical examinations. We became, in a sense, a band of brothers, if you can include wives as "brothers," keeping track of each other's progress, giving and getting cheer about certain medical reactions or developments, including personal affairs. For example, everyone was delighted when Billy Williams had a new Chrysler given to him; Dr. Ring let him start driving a week early. We became transplant ambassadors for St. Paul and other medical centers. One or several of Ring's transplantees (well beyond the original five) has visited every new transplantee as soon as one has reached Intensive Care from the operating room, and the transplant office becomes "the couch" for those waiting for a heart or contemplating a transplant. Wayne Bavol and his wife became active in a regional Heart Beat club, which tries to visit those waiting in hospitals for a heart as well as to contact those who have undergone a transplant. Bob Morgan, an ex-Navy flier, was sixty-four when he got his new heart, and within four months he was giving heart pep talks to his former fellow executives at General Electric Corporation. A transplant patient can become an evangelist, bearing the good news of possibility. It is catching. Dr. Ring says this enthusiasm, this "almost overwhelming ebullience," as he puts it, is to him one of the greatest and finest rewards of successful heart transplantation. (Within two years of its inception, the U. T. Southwestern/St. Paul transplant program under Dr. Ring was doing nearly thirty hearts a year.)

As for public perception, I have had people, strangers, come up and ask if they could touch me, saying something like, "I just want to be able to say I've touched a person who has had a heart transplant!" After the unusualness of transplantation decreases and heart transplants become more common, I'm sure this will change, although even if every candidate were able to get a new heart, there still would be but a tiny fraction of cardiac cases represented. Months after my operation, strangers were still stopping me to tell me, "You're on our prayer list," and ask, "Do you mind?" Did I mind? Anything but. I am a believer in sincere prayer (as opposed to the kind that opens athletic events and civic fund drives). And as for sects and denominations, I wouldn't close any door, no matter what name might be inscribed above it. The persons of several races who told me I was on their prayer list included nuns, priests, and other Catholics (I am a Protestant), as well as rabbis, charismatics, fundamentalists, and Sunday school and Bible classes. I truly believe that the prayers of those dozens, known and unknown, had more than a lot to do with my recovery. Is that just psychological? If so, it works, as far as I'm concerned. The same can be said for the scores of friends, known and unknown, who sent letters, cards, flowers, and gifts from all over the nation—some coming from friends of college days in the 1940s, many I hadn't seen in thirty years, and others who said we had never met but they had read my writings. There were too many for me to thank with a personal reply.

Without my prior knowledge, a group of friends handled a special transplant fund through a Dallas bank, and again the response was overwhelming in both numbers and size of donations. On Betty's advice I did not allow myself to see a list of contributors until several months later because I didn't want to find myself making compari- sons. The fund was a lifesaver; the added support enabled me to avoid worrying about how day-to-day things were to be paid for. Perhaps it isn't germane to talk about money when life and death are waiting to take center ring, but how can you avoid it? The lack of money has led to a number of deaths, and anxiety over its scarcity must surely be a factor in many traumatic situations involving the heart.

During the first three months following transplantation, a heart biopsy is done every two weeks, but after ninety days only once a month, then once every three months, and eventually once a year. Dr. Ring's team continued for a couple of years to experiment with a different form of testing called Magnetic Resonance Imaging (MRI), a process using images produced by placing the body in a strong magnetic field under repeated sound waves that picture the transplanted heart. While MRI was used widely in brain, bone, and muscle studies, this was one of the first times it had been tested as a possible replacement for the biopsy, a development devoutly hoped for by transplantees since the biopsy, while not extremely painful, is the most unpleasant and costly post-op procedure one undergoes. Some found the MRI testing upsetting; you are put in a tunnel-like machine and loud knocking bombards the ears, but often this was the result of claustrophobia brought on from being enclosed as much as from the sound bombardment. Personally, I went to sleep during the thirty minutes or so of MRI testing.

By Southwestern/St. Paul protocol (and I understand heart trans- plant programs are pretty much alike in this respect), on lab days, heart transplant members appear at about 8 A.M. to have vial after vial of blood drawn for all sorts of tests. (And it must be done after "fasting"; that is, nothing can be eaten or drunk after midnight.) Fortunately, I have what are known in the hospital world as "good veins": In my arms they stand out and are easy to find and hit, and they aren't so small they are hidden among the muscles or "collapse" if hit too often. Even after dozens of stickings, my veins remained easily found and flexible. Heart transplant patients, like some other groups that learn to glory in oppression, brag about how many vials of blood they have had drawn at one visit and whether the vials were the small type or the big ones; my record is thirteen of the big-finger-sized vials. Most transplant patients have gone up and down the scale from good to horrid in the skill of the phlebotomist, although medical technology has made several advances in blood collecting in recent years. Now only one needle-stick is needed; the collecting needle remains in the vein and the vials are changed, rather than making a new stick for each vial. And in hospitals today, no needle is used twice, so the old problems of dull or clogged needles seldom arise except through the rare manufacturing flaw. (Of course, the fact that hospital and medical centers in the United States today never reuse apparatus such as syringes, needles, and vials has led to the infamous disposal problems that have caused the littering of seacoast beaches from time to time.)

From the blood lab the transplant patient proceeds to EKG testing and heart X ray, then is weighed and has vital signs taken (blood pressures and heart rate; older readers may recall when TPR—temperature, pulse, and respiration—was the routine), then is worked over by surgeons or specialists who listen and squeeze and prod.

I have gone into some detail here because the fellowship of the transplant group is close and can be very important. Sometimes the thoughts, ideas, annoyances, and observations we share are as valuable to our peace and confidence as what the doctors tell us. It's a relief, for instance, to find that, yes, other transplantees may have to get up several times a night to go to the bathroom or that other ankles swell and feet hurt or legs cramp or funny burning spots inhabit certain regions of the back or that prednisone pones are almost impossible to avoid. This is true among just about all heart transplant people. We are a unique tribe. (I heard of one transplantee who, being chided on some point by his doctor, said gently, "But Doctor, you've never had a transplant.") Like the reunion of old combat soldiers, we don't need to poke around among our emotions; we know. We've played poker with death and come away the winner. When we hear of someone who is scared or stumbling, we gather around, encouraging, coaxing, sympathizing, and in most cases generally being as effective as medicine, because we know what we're talking about. I have discussed it with numbers of transplant survivors in several different programs, and the one thing we all share is a sense of the mystical experience; we brushed death, walked with death, and then returned with only fragments of fearful remembrance. We seldom say it or allude to it in those stark terms, but we have a bond of understanding. Again, this is the general attitude, not just that of one special group. We have come through with an overall feeling that we were renewed; not just the heart and body, but the mind, the soul. Nothing before counted as much as this new life now counts. The "best treatment" is sharing in this experience.

February 14, Valentine's Day, has come to be the unofficial heart transplant holiday, and most groups have a party at their transplant office on this day with fellow transplantees, nurses, surgical teams, folks from the cath lab where biopsies are done, even the blood-stickers. It's very important, the bond of this shared, highly dramatic experience, and the transplant office becomes one's headquarters during those months immediately following the operation—a place you can run to and find advice, a life raft, if you will.

The transplanted person is never well, cured, safe, or however you wish to put it. And the transplant program should remain a constant life raft in the sea of doubt and fear that can so easily sweep over the transplantee from time to time and that, I'm told, never fully relinquishes its threat to contentment.

A heart transplantee should be able to think of himself as special, as unique in the true definition of the word, not one of a dozen or a hundred. Just as a religious convert grows rebellious if suddenly deserted following the high pressure of conversion, so does the transplantee who, having done everything demanded of him and having survived the predicted period of danger, finds the transplant office adopts a "how nice" tone. True, there are a growing number of transplant-veteran organizations from coast to coast that meet regularly and compare notes, give advice, play games, and jolly up with recollections, but to suspect that the surgeon who put the scalpel to your chest has forgotten you, that's beyond disheartening, it's traumatic.

Some heart patients, even after successful surgery, cannot convince themselves they are through the valley of the shadow; and some, working in opposite psychological directions, try to pretend they didn't have a real problem to begin with, that now, after their operation, they can see that the doctors might have been too hasty, made too abrupt a decision to do irreversible procedures, and on and on. (The human mind is the greatest master of sleight of hand of any organism; a fawn can't compare with the mind when it comes to camouflage and protective coloration.) And for a few more heart patients—who immediately consider themselves *ex*-patients—there is an even more dangerous kind of self-deception that assures the patient he or she is not only as good as ever but can return to doing those old things that may have brought on the difficulty to begin with. That self-deception can and often does lead to resumption of cigarette smoking, overeating, or indulging in the wrong foods, going back to the oh-so-innocent "social" drink (or two or three) each lunch and dinner. Plus an extreme case or two of transplant survivors with a God-called-me complex who think follow-up medication is not really necessary, and allowing yourself to be bound by a medical time-frame approaches being sinful: "Faith will move mountains, and it will preserve my heart." God help 'em to define faith better.

In many cases the problems of the problem drinker either stay or come back, even after a transplant operation is successful. This seems to support, partially at least, the disease aspect of the controversial question of whether alcoholism is a disease or a psychological failing. When warned that they may die if they continue to abuse their systems with drugs or tobacco, a surprising number—proportionately—of abusers shrug off the suggestion or are unable to control their addiction . . . and die.

Sadly, many transplant programs find that persons who were alcoholics before their transplant, although stopping while in the hospital or possibly for weeks or even months after discharge, often go back to the bottle for answers, comfort, or whatever the bottle offers if the new life doesn't work out the way it was imagined or the old life returns like an invidious ghost. And with an alcoholic, it often does. That's why organ transplant programs put so much emphasis on compliance, the ability of the patient or would-be transplantee to comply with medical orders, to exercise discipline and self-control.

And this is why I feel so strongly that you should have something internal to hold on to even if it's a relatively frail reed.

There can be all sorts of bizarre responses to transplantation. Although organs may have no race or sex, the human mind can do the job nature doesn't assign, sometimes for good—as when determination answers a medical problem—or sometimes otherwise, when the subconscious creates one. Lee Gutkind, in his book *Many Sleepless Nights,* tells of a male liver transplantee who received a woman's liver, and once out of the hospital, began introducing himself as being "pieced together with my new wife." Later he took to wearing earrings (with portraits of the Virgin Mary engraved on them), and even after two years of an apparently successful transplant, reported he didn't feel "like an integrated person." An alcoholic, he returned to the bottle, began going on binges, and died.

Nearly every transplant coordinator will testify to the fact that difficult recovery (and survival) is not always a matter of how well the operation was performed or in what state the new transplantee left the hospital. Some of the biggest problems come with patients who, in their "old life," were part of high-level management or were self-made men used to giving orders, not taking them—and that's *men* in the gender sense, not the generic. They boast, obviously in error, "I've always been able to control my life, and by God I'll continue to do it," and they can die if continuing to "control my own life" means losing control. The male will find ways to convince himself that, damn it, now that I have a new heart or a newly rebuilt heart, why the hell do I have to keep doing these aerobic exercises, or whatever they call them? This attitude is more apparent in bypass patients than in transplantees, and the difference in attitudes mainly comes (I think) from the dramatic suddenness that transplantation gives to new feelings and emotions. Of course, a successful bypass does invigorate and revitalize a dragging organ, but total replacement seems not just to correct but recreate that "new heart, new start" feeling I've mentioned before.

Perhaps the saddest of the difficult transplant types is the younger patient, especially the teenager. Our youth culture is so obsessed with looks, goaded by the never-sleeping persuasion industry, that the slightest perceived or imagined change in body or face becomes a major crisis, particularly with girls. Some secretly cut back on or cut out their prescribed drugs in terror of the pones or "moonfaces" that can accompany certain medications. This will usually stop the "Cushinging," and because they look better they tell themselves they are feeling better, but most of those who do this end up suffering rejection events, which leads to even more medication and the vicious circle begins.

There have been even sadder cases than those caused by the somewhat understandable errors a young girl might make. One surgeon told me about a sixteen-year-old boy who had a successful heart transplant but who resumed smoking, "partying," and beer drinking as soon as he was back on his feet. The transplant team warned him this was dangerous, finally putting it squarely to him that it meant death. "I don't want to live if I can't enjoy life the way I want to live it," he said. The doctors pointed out that age sixteen was barely the beginning of mature life and that a little caution now could mean many added years. The boy insisted (in the strongest terms) he didn't want to live if it meant giving up "all the fun in life." So he kept his fun for a year or two, but he lost his life. "It was simply suicide," the surgeon said.

Then there is the matter of sexuality: Will a heart transplant diminish my desire? Will I even want to? If so, can I still perform, and at what level? Will various sex acts feel the same to me? After all, a bunch of nerves are cut during the operation, and who knows which ones control what? These are valid questions and normal fears, especially for younger transplanted men (accepting, for this instance, that the physical problem is not the same for a woman). I have found that few doctors or nurses approach this subject without using too many "either-or/perhaps," or other temporizing phrases. And most, if pushed for an answer, will say it depends a lot on the pre-problem sexual capability of the man. Which is true, you know, but doesn't answer the burning question: "What about me *now?*"

And there are little nagging questions, whether spoken or not (questions you may hate yourself for even thinking, they're so paltry): "If I get a woman's heart, will I feel about sex like a woman?" and vice versa, or "Wonder what kind of a guy the donor was sexually?" or "Will a stranger's heart affect my sex personality?"

What I have found, from frank questioning, is that a new heart seems to enhance the sexuality of younger men—including those in their forties, or fifties, perhaps—and may enhance an older man's sexual ability if other factors, such as a vivid sexual imagination, enhance the enhancement. One older transplantee, vigor renewed, told me, laughing, he advised his wife, well past childbearing, that maybe she'd better get back on the pill. But a new heart, strong though it may be, by itself does *not* restore sexual powers that may already have been lost in an older man. For all male transplantees there is a certain danger that medication will either lead to or continue a degree of impotence. Why is this? Very simple: Some of the medication taken by heart transplantees is specifically to reduce blood pressure and thin the blood so that its clotting tendency is lessened. This works counter to the normal operation of the male sexual apparatus. In a younger man sexuality may have declined—impotence, in fact, is common in many cardiac cases—but a new, lustier heart seems to restore much or all that lost power. In an older man, restoration is often a matter of appreciation; it refurbishes more than rejuvenates. On the other hand there is the matter of sexual appetite; older transplantees are sometimes swept by passion but seldom by that alarming physical possession that afflicts younger men, so the matter of lesser performance is not as painful to them.

The general feeling among medical professionals, as most would acknowledge privately, seems to be that men or women over sixty shouldn't really be interested in sex, that by that age they should have made some kind of accommodation which would take the place of sex. When people reach sixty, however, they may feel quite differently. And I know (since I was sixty-four when transplanted) that you get very few answers from younger medical personnel when you start talking about sex after a transplant operation; they simply don't think it's seemly, or maybe they don't think you are any longer eligible to know.

Continuing "Can I? Will I? Dare I?" questions remain in many heart patients' hearts. If I get a new heart or have a bypass operation, will overstrenuous activity bring about problems? From experience I think it safe to assure such questioning heart transplantees that the dire rumors and whispers are to be disregarded. Although sex can and should have a strenuous effect on the participants, it has been pretty well determined that sexual activity alone will not bring on a heart attack or destroy the "new" heart, whether bypass or transplant—within reasonable bounds of good sense, of course, accepting the thought that one who has undergone such surgery is not going to be all that "flat-out" in his or her earliest resumption of sexual activities. And as for age, the level of one's sexuality is governed more by one's imagination and emotions than by physical parameters. The young tend to think sex was invented for use of under-thirties only, and even to talk of it at fifty or more is embarrassing, but let me assure "older" transplantees that, from personal experience, male sexual considerations (I balk at using such prissy terms as "desires" or "urgings") do not depart and may be approached on the same basis as any other vigorous use of the body.

Without quite descending to the entertainment level the thought implies, sex has been determined to be good for you—you being, in our case at hand, the heart transplantee. This doesn't mean you must be a sexual athlete. Medical authorities have reported that if you, as a heart patient, are allowed to walk up two flights of stairs, you can safely enjoy sex. (For those who live in one-story houses: lotsa luck!) Researchers in the relatively recent field of psychoneuroimmunology (or PNI, as it is shortened) have allegedly discovered mechanisms that show good feelings actually start movements in the nervous system which boost the proper operation of the immune system, especially when the good feelings are directed outwardly as well as inwardly. And isn't that as nice a description of sex as you might want? Whether accompanied by strenuous exertion or not, any "total discharge" of the body (even sneezing) involves a "surrender of the ego" that is akin to dying. In this momentary surrender, this fugitive sense of death and rebirth, there is health and spiritual elevation.

Not to take too much of the romance out of things, it was discovered early in the 1970s that there seems to be a literal chemistry of love. Neuropeptides, more than sixty in all, are peptide molecules that flood the body and make your nervous system feel good. The human body produces its supplies of neuropeptides from cells in the brain or in the immune system and nerve endings throughout the body, so that the thought of making love signals one's body to begin releasing these wonderful molecules that operate more powerfully than a drug. Sexier equals healthier, which makes sense.

I approached physical rehab with the notion that I was too old to benefit other than to preserve the very basic functions of life, but I discovered through reading that people who work out have a higher interest in sex no matter what their age. Working out is in itself evidence that you care, either for your body's shape and attractiveness or for your very existence. Not everyone my age is working out with sex in mind, to be sure, but *some* are, and looking around at cardiac rehabilitation sessions would embarrass most of the participants, including me, if it were put solely on that basis. However, a blush doesn't necessarily dismiss what the heart is responding to and the mind is thinking, does it?

Sexual arousal increases the testosterone level in men's blood, and a moderate increase in natural testosterone is known to increase efficient oxygen use, allay depression, and help the immune system. *Esquire* magazine reported that in a 1987 survey conducted by another magazine, young women reported being sexually aroused more easily than usual immediately after exercising. The article didn't suggest what the difference might be between "young" women and "old" women, but you suspect the difference lies more in the mind of the reader than in the results of the psychologists. (But having been young once, you hesitate to think of being young twice, and only the *very* young want to be young forever.) *Esquire* writer John Poppy gives this exercise/arousal business physical validity, positing that physical motions of love involve the pelvis "to which are attached the long muscles that are the body's most powerful . . . and this creates the possibility of strenuous aerobic/anaerobic exercise during sex." So sex and exercise are forms of human activity that, in their actual performance, produce good stress rather than *dis*tress.

Chapter 14

Life is a series of problems; once one is solved you are immediately faced with a problem created by the solution or a new problem for which there is no solution. One answer is to pretend the little trifling things are important and downgrade the big, unconquerable things. That way, you can feel a lift in pride and self-respect when you take care of a problem that has a reasonably simple answer and then shove the towering problem to the side because there seems to be no answer to it. Isn't that a good way for a transplantee to die, someone might ask? You can surely die from big things, of course, but having gone through an enormous thing (in the way of death potential) and survived, the heart transplantee can take the liberty of making a few commonsense, level-headed, cozy rules to live by, post them on the cork board or the refrigerator door of his mind, and turn his attention to the nagging doubts and fears that can be given short-order A-B-C or 1-2-3 answers.

Strange symptoms? They could be anything, but as far as I'm concerned they are nothing, especially if the doctor shakes his head, smiles, raises his eyebrows. No, I'm not going to catch something just from reading about it. Neither am I going to develop something by too much *thinking* about it. An "ignorance is bliss" attitude at this point may be bliss. If that's bravado, well then, bravado just might help you through the minefield—or at least across the desert toward whatever golden heights you think you may observe on the horizon.

Tragedy should be approached in a forgetful frame of mind. For the successful transplant, your big, important problem is keeping alive, holding what you've got. So how do you go about it, what do you do? What you do is (1) nothing stupid, (2) set your $29.95 digital alarm wristwatch for 9 A.M. and 9 P.M., or for whatever times you must take your medications, (3) be sure you have ordered well in advance so you won't run out of cyclosporine, prednisone, or Imuran, (4) do your aerobic exercise even if it's raining, you're sleepy, and you have a house load of visitors, (5) eat the way the nutritionist told you to and that you know you should, and then (6) forget you carry this big, rest-of-your-life burden and worry about things such as whether or not you need to buy a new front tire for your wife's car, if some professional should come clean the carpet in that bedroom where your daughter kept her dog for two weeks, why your waist size has ooched up and a size 34 squeezes you like Rhett Butler lacing up Scarlett O'Hara, whereas a size 36 has to be pleated in the rear. Worry about things you can solve with a checkbook or a phone call.

Problems. Problems. You would think, wouldn't you, that a transplantee's problems were over once he came out of the OR, got out of ICU, left the hospital, did a few biopsies, gave a few gallons of blood and urine, and was cleared for takeoff, so to speak. You would think, perhaps, that thanksgiving, joy, and satisfaction to be alive were the only symptoms left after the medical ordeal. But something in us doesn't appreciate equilibrium, especially spiritual equilibrium. We want to have to shoulder some kind of burden even if it's only a burden of guilt. We just can't seem to let our soul take its ease. And in that situation I'll confess I've always felt a bit of sympathy for the rich man in the biblical parable who one evening looked over his barns, noted they were chock-full, decided to build bigger ones, and said to himself (never dreaming that someone named Luke would put it on record), "Soul, take thine ease, eat, drink, and be merry." What should we expect a man like that to do? Wouldn't I have done the same thing, said the same thing, in his place? And doesn't the heart transplantee, passing one of those safety-zone milestones, have the right to express soul satisfaction? But then we who faithfully attended Sunday School remember that God scorned the would-be barn-builder and told him that he wouldn't last the night. How do you think that fits into a transplantee's soul? Awkwardly, that's how, except I have a notion that God might overlook a certain amount of soul satisfaction on the part of the transplantee after ninety days or six months or a year, but maybe not the eat, drink, and be merry part.

One big problem with the recovering or waiting heart patient is the tendency to place so much importance not just on the other partner but on the institute of marriage itself, as though it too were a transplant program from which you should emerge reconstituted. I don't know why it is that so many people of both sexes (I tend to think in male terms, of course) believe that marriage, one way or another, is the key to so many situations. You have a problem? Get married or get unmarried; either can seem to be the solution. One would think that after ten or twenty years of sharing life with some-one there would be no way that half of you had caused so much unhappiness as seems to settle over you when you wait for something the way you must wait for a heart. Impatience should only character-ize the honeymoon. Perhaps it is because survival is in question, or maybe your feelings are the reverse of blame, seeking by means of self-accusation to close rather than widen the gulf of emotion, with love impelling the notion of blame, "I" being the one to blame for letting "myself" get weak and helpless. Forgive me for something I did that I shouldn't have done, something I could have kept from doing or could have undone; I'm to blame and not the partner.

Here again it is hard for me to see how such misunderstanding can be based on what I believe is the supreme form of understanding: long-shared lives. Who knows me better than my spouse? Certainly not my brothers and sisters or even my own children. And the spouse almost invariably knows you better than you know yourself, or knows parts of you that you don't know at all. (A philosophical aside: I think a successful marriage is also based on the mystery of the sexes; the differences that come from being male and female are magnetic attractions. Can a man ever understand a woman in the same ways another woman can? While this idea can be adapted to males,

masculine differences are usually less particularized and more gener-
alized, therefore more easily inspected or rejected by the inspector:
"I don't *need* to know some things about men!" A woman is mysterious to a man; a man can be merely odd to a woman. Years of living
with each other only heightens and never dilutes this feeling.)

Strange things can happen with any sort of heart involvement.
Betty had a pacemaker implanted a few weeks after I had a heart
transplant—she claimed she caught heart trouble from me. During
the implant operation, which is generally a short procedure under
local anesthesia, she had to have a general anesthetic administered
and became convinced that the pacemaker specialist was standing on
her chest with one foot while propping the other on the ceiling in
an attempt to install the pacemaker mechanism. Even when the
cardiologist, the pacemaker installer, and I all laughed at her story,
and the specialist, who was a rather short man, assured her he not
only had *not* stood on her chest but couldn't have reached the ceiling
with his other foot if he had, I'm not sure she was convinced.

One night some weeks later, after having dinner with us, Bill Kraus
noticed her right shoulder twitching in regular rhythm. Her pacemaker seemed to be propelling that upper muscle as well as regulat-
ing her heartbeat. What was wrong? Somehow, possibly in her sleep,
the pacemaker had flipped itself over and was pounding on the
muscle's nerve. Not being used to such machinery, she thought
perhaps that kind of action was to be expected. Other than waking
her up from time to time with its pulsation, it did no harm and was
easily flipped back to its correct position without surgery by the
pacemaker specialist.

Convalescence, like waiting, can be a most dangerous time, dangerous to more than just the patient. It is a testing time, a time when
love and affection are often stretched to their limits. Or can we
stretch "true love" to some "limit"? Can there be an acceptable
definition of true love? More often than not, after the heart patient
has waited and then received his new heart and is on the road to
recovery, he (speaking in the generic sense, you understand) will be
the one who forgets all the friction, disillusionment, and threats that
might have arisen, no matter how wildly and often, during the

treacherous waiting period. Betty's journal describes that change in a positive way: "A.C. says our lives are all going to be different because of his change of attitudes. He's tired of being a cynic, talking down people when he doesn't really know them. He is truly like a different person."

But sometimes the victim turns out to be Patient Griselda herself, the wife who, having suffered through mood changes, personality erosion, and bitter visions on the part of her husband, can't overcome those dark memories even after the husband has reversed all the evidences of depression, fear, and unhappiness. (I'm pleased to quote my wife's more joyful feelings: *"The* momentous day we've been waiting for—the day we got a new heart for A.C.") Sometimes Patient Griselda decides, now that he's safe, she wants out. That's why it is so important to gain some kind of acceptable view of the process, no matter what the particular disease or affliction might be. All sides of the occasion must know that it will almost surely happen, to some degree or another, but that recovery will, ninety-nine times out of a hundred, wipe away the ugly stains on the relationship that seemed so permanent. Before-and-after comparisons are also danger-ous unless they are offered as evidence of deliverance, helping to understand that we are no longer dealing with the "old" him or her. Don't forget: new heart, new start.

Not too surprising, perhaps, recovery can sometimes lead to bit-terness. I have met older men who complained that once they had succeeded in regaining some of their lost ability after their heart transplant, their families began to treat them as if they were again in their thirties or forties. They ended up, as they saw it, doing all the work, all the things you were supposed to have done *for* you after you reached retirement age. One man in his sixties said he had three children, and every year they got a little younger, and now they expected him to continue to perform all the emotional and physical functions he had performed as their father when they were growing up.

"After I get older, really old and really helpless, what am I going to do?" he asked. "Who's going to take care of me? They don't know how. Everything has appeared by magic when Daddy waved the magic wand. 'What have you brought me, Daddy?' didn't stop at age eight, it didn't stop at age eighteen. Now at twenty-eight, thirty-eight, it hasn't stopped yet." That plaint isn't confined to transplantees, as we know. But it is one aspect of the different interpretations that can be applied to such topics as recovery, new life, and new start when, from time to time, none of the above can be fully instituted. A new life for one person is not necessarily a new life for all those around him. That new start I've mentioned so much isn't always new and isn't always a start. Sometimes it's an old resumption.

Another problematic development can take place. That's the faultfinding attitude some patients bring home after a hospital stay, especially if the hospital stay was longer than ordinary. For example, at home I began to make comparisons with the way things were done in the hospital—little things: My bedroom is not as tidy as my hospital room was; the air conditioning is too hot/too chilly; the sheets don't smell right; is that dust on the television screen? And my cry of the day became, "You know I'm *not* supposed to do that" or the second verse, "You know I *am* supposed to always . . ." That cry can include everything from the way my medication was presented to the kind of food I was offered. Hospital food may be traditionally bad, but even bad food becomes tolerable when every meal comes at the same time, delivered on a tray with all the little things you so frequently forget at home: imitation salt, a knife ("The hospital *always* brought a knife. . . ." "But I didn't think you needed a knife with a bowl of oatmeal"—I'm quoting from memory!), a napkin, a pat of margarine, pepper, that ever-present little container of jelly, and that tightly sealed plastic cup of juice.

And not all hospital food is bad by any means. Sometimes this fact causes comparisons to be made too easily once you are home, comparisons in favor of the hospital, especially if you were served one or two special dishes that you liked more than usual. In my own case at St. Paul, I was twice served, on the "healthy heart" menu, chicken Kiev, which was delicious although low in salt. Betty tried to find it in grocery stores, health food stores, and even in high-priced specialty gourmet boutiques, but without success. I had a nutritionist at the hospital inquire of the kitchen whence cometh the dietetically marvelous, delicious chicken Kiev. The nutritionist reported that as near as she could find out, it came frozen only in boxes of dozens or so. My wife volunteered to prepare her own chicken Kiev, but it is not a chore to be taken lightly or in single batches, so, disgruntled, recovering ex-victim though I was, I ceased making comparisons. (Success! Over a year later, after giving a talk to the hospital's emeritus M.D. club, I was presented with a box of frozen chicken Kievs as my honorarium.)

Speaking of hospitals and food, women can't seem to accommodate themselves to hospital food with the same ease a man can. Surely it is in the nature of the beast and his appetite. Betty couldn't believe that I actually enjoyed hospital meals, even when I tried to qualify my liking with "Well, I liked breakfast—as long as somebody didn't try to microwave the bread." She couldn't see how I could eat any of it, or words to that effect. And later, when she was in the hospital having her pacemaker implanted, I visited during mealtime and pointed out how much I liked this dish or that concoction, and finished off her tray, never able to get her to agree about anything more than the fresh grapes. She didn't even like the institutional orange juice. Well, all that's not quite correct. She liked the St. Paul coffee. She said it was better than she made at home, which I considered to be nonsense, but I agreed it was good and, wondrously, always seemed to arrive hot.

Getting back to work or shaping a new routine for your life usually takes care of the cardiac blues unless something is not working medically and your depression is keyed to a situation over which you have less control than you might have over your vocation or profession. I find that a thrice-weekly workout keeps me in shape in more ways than one. I can mold my week around these three mornings and, fortunately, being a professor with a great deal of flexibility in his schedule, can usually make my timetables work without having to give in to that frantic rush with which many of us start Monday morning.

It's better to be a white-collar worker because you don't have to go back to doing heavy work. If the alternative is starving to death, however, what choice have you? Some corporations have extra-training programs for transplantees who can work again but can't do the heavier type work they had done before their operation. A younger member of our transplant group returned to his former vocation, managing a security service. He didn't have to walk patrol, but he did have to be moving around, in and out of his car, checking and assigning workers. Another, also a few years younger, went back to working as a butcher. So having a heart transplant does not mean you are condemned to sitting at a desk or in an easy chair. In fact, to have gone through the transplantation process may enhance certain jobs, such as teaching. It could make you a better teacher. The stress of the classroom is still there, but transplant philosophy offers a means of self-control that in most cases wasn't operating before the heart ordered the individual to slow down.

In light of some other transplantees, I guess I'm lucky that I was able to return to working as quickly as I did and also to do as *much* work, both as a teacher and as a writer. I read a book and did a review of it for a Florida newspaper less than a month after I'd left the hospital, and I was back in the classroom teaching a rather large roomful of graduate students and keeping campus office hours within two months of surgery. (If this sounds like a niggling example of rapid recovery, recall, there was a time, and not very far removed from today, when a heart transplantee was required not just to go slow but never to work again; remember the case of the French longevity record holder who survived a transplant eighteen and a half years but never returned to his job after the operation was performed.)

I decided I was immensely glad that the dress code in American academic society, even in Texas, has relaxed so that the necktie and suit are options. Chancellors, presidents, provosts, and others who daily face the nonacademic public at such joyful occasions as state legislative budget hearings and high-level attempts to gain a bit more money through corporate or government grants have to wear the three-piece uniform with one of poet Eliot's neckties "rich and modest." But as a classroom professor you can wear Reeboks or Adidas or almost anything you want—you don't even have to keep up with the teenagers' choice of styles and trademarks.

For the first class I taught after my heart transplant (catalogue title: Creativity) I wore a pair of rugged half-boots, a reasonably wild jungle vest, and designer khaki pants, along with a saffron yellow wrinkled shirt (made to look like peasant garb so everyone would know it was costlier) and a handmade necklace, or pectoral garnishment, sent me by the maker as a get-well present, consisting of several very nice ancient flint pieces strung on brown fishing cord and separated by white dried rattlesnake vertebrae. Since few of the students knew me (it had been two semesters since I had last taught) I walked into the room and immediately had them write what they thought about me—what I did, what I liked, the kind of person I was. I thought I was pulling an amusement on them because their essays persisted in designating me as either an environmentalist, a "digger" (archaeologist), a Native American specialist, or at least an (untitled) *activist,* and one student expressed the half-conviction that I was the last of the Great White Hunters left over from Ernest Hemingway's camp at Mount Kilimanjaro. But it was I who learned. The answers taught me a lesson: Today you are what you wear. If I really were an environmentalist, a digger, or a white hunter, I probably *would* wear just about what I had on. It certainly would catch the TV camera's eye.

But I don't relate this little episode to evidence cleverness or new ways of pedagogy. I tell it to show that such an epiphany as returning from the other side of the blank wall can become an act of release, freeing the new person from his old personality. The successful heart transplantee grows to feel that *now* he is bulletproof. Having survived a real physical danger, he is more willing to expose himself to social and cultural "dangers" he wouldn't have dreamed of had he continued the way he was. The transplant survivor can express himself a shade more honestly than before, not to mention the fact that, like me, an older transplantee is released and rehabilitated and at the same time taught a lesson about the necessity, as Texas writer Frank Dobie declared, of being a contemporary of himself.

I used to be much more of a formalist myself, devoted for twenty years to the uniform of coat, tie, and suit pants. But something about the combination of age and one's delight in surviving the slings and arrows, and so forth, seems to reduce daily situations to their essentials. I'm sure I can be fooled, but I hope it is impossible for me to fool myself. I do have principles, however. I draw the line for myself at wearing or giving or being seen in the presence of T-shirts and sweat suits bearing cute or not-so-cute clichés such as "Sexy Senior Citizen" or "Baby," with an arrow pointing to the obvious.

Quite a few transplantees (and other open-heart surgery patients) are older or retired. This may be a factor in survival, in contrast to the professional impatience of some younger men who quite often have to give up chosen employment and are unable to get back into the job market in the niche they formerly occupied. This is undoubt- edly a curse, in most instances, but on closer inspection it can become a blessing. I have talked to younger transplantees who said they were able, under the impetus of survival, to get out from under a job they'd held for years but never enjoyed. Some of them got into happier vocational situations and credited their transplant situation with forcing them to make a move they might have delayed for years or forever. Although I have talked to vast numbers of transplantees, I have not encountered any of them who felt the process had caused their vocational lives to be ruined or even damaged. It sidetracked some, I am sure, but it renewed more often than it caused the transplantee to have to be rescued.

Reaccommodating oneself to the job, or vice versa, can be as difficult as restructuring one's diet. Work can also interfere with cardiac rehabilitation. Not everyone can meet a fixed weekly or daily schedule of exercise, and it takes a good bit of self-control or remem- bering to set up a convenient medication schedule, especially for such drugs as cyclosporine which not only must be kept reasonably cool and taken very close to the targeted time but also should be taken with milk, chocolate milk, or some other agent with enough butterfat to get the dosage metabolized quickly. When the alterna- tive to mussing up your medication schedule can be death, however, you have no choice, and even careless individuals who have spent a lifetime giving themselves excuses for not doing things are forced to come to grips with necessity under these circumstances.

Also, a rehabilitation program isn't always the highway to restora- tion and salvation. Although I think my age helped me when ap- proaching and accepting some of the disabilities, it could also erect a mental roadblock. When I began supervised cardiac rehabilitation, I feared I might become an old guy like the one in that famous 1970s poster pictured as a twisted, broken, but smiling ancient propelled by some miraculous means along what appeared to be a dusty highway, the caption reading, "Keep on truckin'!" This annoying fear (which gained credence despite my reminding myself that I was superior to such doubts) persisted for nearly two months. Gradually I overcame it, until today I don't even think of that reaction when I work out. But my conviction was far from stable at first.

On reaching my sixth month after the operation, I felt a sense of triumph. I felt that I had singlehandedly defeated something almost as big as death. Death is always out there, beckoning us with the stick and carrot of old age. But defeating the panic and intimidation of the Valley of the Shadow, that was enough to give me the sweet taste of success. The day I went into the "once every three months" routine of post-op maintenance, I felt a great lifting of my shoulders, on one hand, but a feeling of uneasiness, not quite bewilderment, not quite bafflement, on the other. I had been in the daily, weekly, biweekly routine so long and had depended on it so much, in this new life of my heart, that suddenly to be told "Go for it!" was almost like throwing a child into the water and saying, "Take off for the shore!" I did not take off for the shore by any means, but it was a wondrous day for me, a very powerful day, a day that will probably stay with me until the other side of that next mountain when I hope to accept the idea that if I walk carefully through the briars, I can feel free of the constant danger of rejection.

But what does "free" mean to a heart transplantee? As I write, five years is the unexpressed expectation you can more or less count on *if* the first year has passed. Since the cyclosporine era began, circa 1984, not enough time has passed to enable anyone to predict a reliably prolonged statistical future for transplantees. The longest surviving heart transplant (as I write) has been about twenty years, which means the majority of those years came before cyclosporine was in use. If guaranteed twenty years but no more, most of us, before entering the operating room, would unhesitatingly settle for it. But few of the younger transplantees, I suspect, feel twenty years must inevitably be the limit of their remaining time.

There is usually a subtle difference in the acceptance stance of the older transplant patient and the younger one; the young patient often feels he is losing ten or fifteen years of his life while the older patient almost invariably feels he is *gaining* ten or fifteen years. If this validly translates into anything, it is in the matter of recuperation. The older transplant patient tends to do as the professionals say and to have little trouble giving up old, bad habits, whereas, as has been noted before, the younger the transplant patient (except for children), the more likely he or she is to feel the regrets of loss. A transplant surgeon laughed and told me he was thinking about putting a sixty-year age limit on heart transplants. A ceiling? he was asked. No, a sixty-year *floor*, he said; his luck with the latter had been so good.

Chapter 15

So here I am, living from year to year instead of minute to minute or day to day. What can I eat or *not* eat? Do or not do? Is my daily plan of existence different from all other heart transplantees, or am I typical of the class? Of what does my day, my week comprise? What kind of life do I lead, what kind of life is it *possible* for me to lead?

Some writers have proposed the transplantee can never return to a normal life-style, but one's definition of normal is perhaps the key to the answer. If by normal we mean not having to pay any attention to diet, medication, or physical acts, then the answer is no. Rejection of a transplanted organ is (at this point in medical advancement) a constant threat. And at this point every successful transplant pivots around a large amount of medication taken daily, and they are powerful medications. And they are *life*. Sometimes I stop to look at the pills and tablets in my prescription cup or take up the small brown bottle of cyclosporine and think just how powerful they are: the immunosuppressants cyclosporine, azathioprine (Imuran), prednisone (steroid); even the more "usual" drugs such as dipyridamole, sulfamethoxazole-trimethoprim (Bactrim), nifedipine (Procardia), enalapril (Vasotec), and furosemide (Lasix). How much damage, even death, they could deliver were I to under- or overdo them a few times. I know better, of course, but I have become so familiar with them I cannot imagine they could be anything but salvatory, much the way, I suppose, that a diabetic looks upon the daily needle thrust. To me they are life, as necessary and as automatic as breathing, drinking water, or taking in food. Again, side effects from medication aren't always as severe as some reports would offer, implying that because of medications a transplantee's return to normality "is virtually impossible." Without question, advancements will be made in medication, and the time will certainly come when a transplantee will not have to gulp down twenty or more tablets, pills, capsules, or fluid doses every day as most do now.

As this is being written I feel better than I have in ten or even a dozen years. I laugh and tell people I may feel better than I've felt in twenty years except I can't remember how I felt twenty years ago. It's as much a matter of feeling joy as feeling "better." Better than what? A transplantee doesn't feel the necessity to compare; better is equal to good or best to a recovered transplantee. Joy is the ingredient that is missing in so much of our lives as we advance up the ladder of years. We do things with automatic, thoughtless response. We give up so much that life doesn't really demand we give up. We forget to laugh or forget even to *try* to laugh. We leave joy out of the equation. Don't you remember how good it felt as a child when you got up on a summer morning, looked out at the sunny, colorful world, and felt a wonderful twist in your chest and your stomach? Joy . . . pure joy. I think if we could keep having those funny little twists the rest of our lives we'd all live longer and certainly happier—pure joy, the essence of satisfaction, the substance of satisfaction with ourselves. I took a guest to a gathering of twenty-one of Dr. Ring's Dallas heart transplantees and afterward she told me she was inspired by them. "They shared a kind of tranquil exaltation," she said, "living in the moment and joyously demonstrating new life."

A few months after I received my second heart I talked by telephone to my aunt Gertrude, who was approaching her eighty-seventh birthday. She was wheelchair-bound, and when first answering my call, she complained that her pacemaker was doing too good a job because it was keeping her alive when she was "ready to go." But Aunt Gertie, never a morose person, was highly independent and always ready to laugh at a joke or any comical development in the course of affairs (much more so than her sister, my mother). By the time our lengthy telephone conversation ended we had both been laughing, remembering events and celebrations that took place forty, fifty years before, each of us bringing up some ridiculous, awkward, silly incident we'd been involved in, separately or together. At the end of the call, there was a new person on each end of the conversation. We were filled with and sharing joy. She was still very close to eighty-seven and still in her wheelchair, but she was looking forward to reading a magazine article and some genealogical material I was sending her; she had forgotten her physical disabilities and recovered her innate spirit of exuberance, all because she had laughed for a little while. And I had, too.

With a couple of exceptions, I say it is possible for me to lead any sort of life I choose that doesn't violate the bounds of good sense. The exceptions? As noted, I was forbidden to play violent games such as basketball, handball, and football for the first couple of years after the transplant. I suppose other sports such as badminton and racquet ball could be added to that list, not so much because of their effect on a new heart but because of what the violent twisting, turning, and spinning around might do to the incision or internal patchwork. Heart transplantees who so desire seem to be able to get back into even these vigorous sports after a couple of years. And golf—especially the cart kind—is possible for the transplantee within a much shorter time.

Sports isn't everything in life despite the great American tendency to make it seem that way. I don't have to avoid people or public situations that move along normal paths. No alcohol for me, as stated earlier, although I find that is also a personal decision after the first year—alcohol in modest amounts. Some heart transplantees move quicker than that, especially after the first ninety days, and allow themselves a glass or two of wine or champagne on festive occasions or a bottle or two of beer. I'm not sure if any of them, at the ninety-day point, go so far as to resume drinking on the Scotch and water or martini level, but I rather suspect that if they do, it's done on the sly, and the guilt feelings thus laid on them may have as much to do with their downfall, if it comes, as does the liquor.

I just don't do any recreational drinking of anything with alcohol in it. My decision doesn't involve high moral standards or religious beliefs; it comes purely from medical opportunity. Opportunity? Yes. When offered an opportunity to avoid something that is question-able—and alcohol always is, especially to a heart transplantee—then I prefer to opt out. I like Mexican and Chinese foods with beer (and I dearly loved Mexican and Chinese beer), but I am content to stick with no-alcohol malt beverages. There are a number such no-alcohol "beers," and they are suitable substitutes for the real thing, especially if you are one of those persons who must have that malt taste with certain kinds of food—and I'm one who does. (I found the no-alcohol malt beverage Texas Select brand even up in Maine and in several New York West Village bars.)

Don't let me get away with sounding like I'm so upright I can't bend over to tie my shoes. Liquor just doesn't happen to be one of my weaknesses, even though I was once famed across Texas for my martinis. Also, you are hereby permitted to note that I haven't dwelt overlong on how you handle a few foods such as ice cream or salted nuts. I used to say (pretransplant) that if I died and went to heaven, I wanted to be able to have ice cream, Mexican food, and beer every day without gaining weight or eating my way into a convalescent home.

I also shrug off eggs, even though the transplantee is allowed one, two, or three eggs with yolks per week. I love eggs and especially like to whip up my own inventive omelets (even when my ever-loyal wife was the only family member who would eat them), but again, it's an opportunity to avoid temptation since I can live without eggs and not miss them so much that it becomes a nagging problem. You can get imitation eggs, but that's skating on fairly thin ice for me, a gour-mand as well as a gourmet. Angel food cake made with egg whites? Certainly. I embrace the idea—and half the cake, if I'm not careful. But eggs join the list of foods I do without without missing them.

Do I have a hard time eating out in fine and fancy restaurants? Of course I do, but that's not confined to transplantees. And I have found that after those crucial first ninety days, the menus offer several dishes that won't send your heart or blood pressure over the top. However, I would caution those who want to pursue this thought a bit further: Don't order a $35 fish dish and then tell the chef, via the waiter, to hold the sauce. Remember, $30 of that dish is in the sauce and the chef's reputation, so you lose both ways. You do want the maître d' to remember your name the next time you bring someone aboard for a power meal, don't you?

Everything that might have concerned me during my first weeks following the transplant I had accepted after a year: the need for rest—six hours per night aren't always enough, plus a nap some days, especially after working out or laboring out of doors, even if carefully confining such work to the shade. The bushy quality of my hair, following use of cyclosporine, no longer interests me after a lifetime of finer fleece on my head. My Hungarian female barber is delighted with the change. In addition to having more of it, my hair has regained a certain amount of color, although being born blond, silver threads among the gold have never shown me up as gray-headed as I am.

My same disregard goes for the various numb places on my body. One spot on my back worried me considerably the first sixty days or so after the transplant (a surgeon soberly suggested if the spot were shingles I should be readmitted to the hospital and a heavy emergency regimen of steroids begun, which quickly got my mind off the worrisome spot, you can bet). Now the suspect spot comes and goes and so does my concern about it and the other disappearing and reappearing numb places.

Self-indulgence? I do seem to need more rest. Certain parts of me hurt, and that marvelously acute hearing I bragged to myself I had seems to have lessened without my noticing. (They say that those growing deaf are the last to realize it.) I find myself asking students to speak up, although some of them look puzzled when I say it since they claim to have been speaking in a near shout. I doubt it; students today, even graduate students, are great mumblers. Age may be the problem, and if so, I have it. But I don't have dandruff, I haven't had the flu, and I haven't had shingles or herpes.

Yes, it gets tiresome constantly having to remind myself to do one thing and not do another, but exercise and dieting are not things that I particularly want to avoid. I look forward to exercise on most days, and I've always been the kind of eater who could be happy on a rather limited menu, which is not to say I don't like wonderful rich sauces or crème brûlée, but I also can live on dried breakfast foods almost

365 mornings out of the year. Give me half a banana or possibly a quarter melon, and I can start the day on it. Am I beginning to sound heroic again? There's nothing heroic about surviving after a heart transplant; it's a matter of discipline once that first safety zone has been passed through. Fear keeps you pretty much on the straight and narrow before then. Once you feel safer, the body, with all its appetites and indulgences, strives to take over again; only the will can reject the advances with which the body tempts its owner, with the sudden declarations and impulses that threaten to become compulsions, unacknowledged but strongly asserted. If you say you have no will, that you don't see how you could give up things such as cigarettes, alcohol, or fried anything, then I would suggest you make sure you come from heart-hearty stock because you sure will have a time making it through heart transplant and surviving long enough to enjoy it.

To the question "How do you really feel?" I say, without hesitation, "Great." I don't do long-distance work, I don't do sustained heavy work. No, I don't do ten miles at top speed on the treadmill, and I don't pump enough iron to have to buy body oil to get ready for photographs. I do a maintenance schedule that for a man my age is very good. Added to a mile or more of walking, I work out three times a week on sixteen machines, including one that exercises the calf muscles only. And I feel systemically great and have been feeling great for many months now.

A question, or attitude, that continues to be asked about or shown toward transplantees involves activities and ways of life. The same week in which I read a newspaper account of a twelve-year-old girl heart transplantee whose father warned her, "You shouldn't do that 'cause you're not like normal people," I also read about a twenty-four-year-old European professional soccer player who had had a heart transplant at age twenty-one, who was the number-one draft pick of an American soccer club. I emotionally took my hat off (although I seldom wear a hat) to the twelve-year-old who says that when her father warns her about not being normal, "I fly off the handle. The only difference is I take ten different medicines and I have a little incision in my chest. But that's all." It's not all, but it's near enough to being "all" that it's a realistic answer to warnings such as her father offered. Since I am a father myself, I know the advice was given in love and not in reproof, but it was shocking. When the twelve-year-old reaches age twenty-four, she, too, will have long before discovered how "like normal people" she's become.

This quality of normality seems the last frontier of transplant development; it remains an abstruse, almost unattainable proposition in the minds of too many medical professionals. And the advice they give often mirrors this obscurity, causing them to present transplantation more as an experimental prospect than as a statistically measurable operation. The reality of it is that organ transplant is no longer strictly a rearguard action that leaves the recipient alive but forevermore enfeebled. Even as recent a time as the tail end of the 1980s has seen transplantation rapidly evolve toward a restoration rather than a salvage operation. Forward movement in human life never stops. We can be amused at the outlandish idea that the brain or the entire human head might be transposed, medically, but I am sure that if an archivist a century or so from now digs into some molding copies of this work, that twenty-first- or twenty-second-century archivist will be even more amused that we were bemused at the prospect; that it will be a practice on or above the level with today's heart, liver and heart/lung transplants. Remember, our imaginations seldom can keep up with our inventions: man always figured someday he would fly, but he couldn't have imagined it would be in eighteen- and nineteen-ton metal birds.

People still ask me questions about every facet of the heart transplant experience. Due to my public exposure as a columnist and writer, I get referrals, you might say, from people who are facing or have loved ones who are facing some kind of transplant operation. I try to be helpful, and if the questions are innocent enough, that is, nonmedical, I give answers from experience. In general I am encouraging, especially if it is someone who knows decisive steps must be taken sooner or later. I try to let the questioners see that *sooner* is not an admission of surrender to anything; it's just being realistic. Heart transplant, *any* transplant, is a dangerous operation. What you read about are the successes. What you don't read about are the failures, not that anyone is trying necessarily to cover the failures. The successes are *so* successful, however, that they overcome the failures, which in the general run of things, I expect, is the

way it should be. There is enough fear even in approaching the
subject (recall my trepidation) without being told how many didn't
make it or made it in worse shape than they went in.

There is no such thing as a standard case—a standard recovery or
a standard medication system; although certain health bureaucrats
might like to handle them in that manner, things don't work out that
way. Even the aptest comparison doesn't always hold up when it
comes to your situation.

What about this matter of psychological dependency? Don't you
tend to take too much of your recovery on faith? There's something
to the thought, of course. But faith is more reliable than proof, which
can (and does) change from year to year or week to week. I can look
back at minor changes in the way heart transplants are handled and
notice several small changes, but it doesn't upset me; my faith has
carried me through the personal changes without demanding proof.
I believe in the medications I take—the ones I don't know about,
the ones I haven't checked up on—and take them as a matter of
faith. Some, such as cyclosporine, I recognize as vital to my survival,
and although I don't know the absolute medical proofs involved in
their use, I don't question the need to take them, so it's not so much
a matter of faith or psychology as it is conviction: I want to live!

I take certain medications because they're prescribed; I'm not sure
what they do, I'm not sure the doctor knows everything they *might*
do, but their beneficial responses must override their deficits because
they haven't done anything *bad* to me and that is *good.* Some other
medications are preventatives that have been proved to work in
certain conditions my disability is heir to—such as baby aspirin (now
called low-dose aspirin so as not to embarrass the mature patient—or
is it to make the name more palatable and thereby sell more aspirin?).
I also take a vitamin tablet each day and calcium supplements; maybe
they aren't needed, maybe they are more placebo than prescription,
but why worry about taking them? They don't cost that much and,
who knows, any one of those "placebos" may be what's keeping me
alive.

The point is now, today, whatever your age, it's how you feel, not
how many pages you've covered in your journal of time. What is age,
incidentally, in relation to the heart and those delicate medical

procedures? Or what is time that we are so conscious of it? Why save it? Why think we will lose it if we fail to inject every second of it as it passes? What shape is time? When does it count most: yesterday, today, or tomorrow? Time passes us or we pass time. It doesn't stand still and neither do we; it's go or stop.

Regardless of your state of health, time replaces most of the quotidian emotions once considered irreplaceable. Look how much your position can change in a single day, thinking one thing at breakfast, turning 180 degrees by nightfall. That same thought holds true of regrets. Of course there are regrets, not regrets that a heart transplant was done or that I must keep such close watch on so many daily things, but regrets that many opportunities in my "other" life were passed over—not merely overlooked, passed over. We don't stumble through life so much as we dodge and weave, like a pedestrian on a crowded sidewalk, twisting, turning, avoiding contact. Only when we see someone we want to touch do we stop, smile, and in a figurative sense via the handshake, seize our opportunity. That loss of chance (and I don't believe I am alone in this) symbolizes the kind of regret we "new life" people feel. We dodged so many opportunities. We could have formed a friendship or at least shared a handshake.

Opportunity: When I was younger I said that life is all a matter of timing, that it is as if we are in a many-roomed hotel walking down a long hall with anonymous doors on either side, and every once in a while one of those doors will suddenly open and a hand will reach out and grab us or miss us; it depends on timing. I no longer believe that. I'm always romantic enough to think that fate, kismet, or what you will, can operate in wonderfully delightful ways, but I no longer think that all of life is in timing. As we walk down that long, door-lined corridor often as not we are afraid to look at those anonymous doors. One of them might turn out to have our name on it, and where would that door lead? The lady or the tiger? So we hurriedly convince ourselves there's no need (or no sense) to look. We tell ourselves that if there is a name like ours on a door, it's probably misspelled or it's some other person with a similar name. And we hurry by, looking straight ahead so we won't have to investigate or (God forbid!) make a decision.

You lose much of that kind of repression when you have done the transplant adventure. You know something you didn't know before. You have found a person living beside you all those years for whom you had few thoughts even when you briefly or out of the corner of your eye glimpsed his or her presence in the mirror of contemplation. I hasten to add that this changed perception is not motored by the presence of someone else's body part, or might it be? Persons who have lost limbs sometimes speak of phantom pains or seeming reactions to parts that are no longer there; might the process in some way be reversed? No, it (probably) isn't. But it's one of those intriguing bubbles of reflection that pop up from time to time.

I am not speaking in a metaphysical way when I speak of that person in the mirror. One thing I have become convinced of from talking with dozens of transplantees is that the process leads to change, great change, without and within—especially within. It is not a matter of rededication or spiritual realization; the human animal seems not to handle either of these ideas very well over any period of time. It is a matter of *change:* You are not the same, you do not have the same outlook on life or death. Your body and its functioning may be changed (let's hope so) by the newly transplanted organ (or organs, as is now often the case), but *you* aren't changed just by it or them. *You* are changed by something that medical science still can't put its gloved finger on—call it soul, call it mind, call it "heart" in that ancient, still useful sense. The *you* that was is not the *you* that is, and the you that *is* rapidly distances itself from the you that *was.* It is almost a rebirth. The life you lived "before" seems to be someone else's life. And (making a personal observation now) you seem to have lost a great deal of interest in him and it.

We have all heard that money will not buy happiness, but neither will it buy a state of mind. How do you achieve peace or a truce with yourself in the face of doubt, fear, and uncertainty? It takes a test, a test you must give and pass to and for your own satisfaction. And internal convictions as well as fears must also face tests. You can't ward off fear, you can't confront terror, you can't know about yourself by basing any of it on the use of or the abundance of money. Now the critical period is past; the heart has accepted me and I have accepted my heart. The fear would have been there if I had owned the wealth of a billionaire; the sense of new life, new start came without fiscality.

Other potential physical disasters didn't scare me. Passing the test of self-reliance during waiting and recuperation rid me of that bent to resignation. I will not be grimly resigned to *everything* life holds from now on. If I can't always wrestle the angel, maybe I can at least keep time marching to my drum/heartbeat rather than letting time mold my life.

"Circumstances alter cases," may be such a cliché that it has lost its meaning, but whole lives can change with the circumstances of one day. Thus it is or *usually* is with someone who has had an organ transplant. The person who was pushed into the OR will not be the same person who is pushed out, and most definitely will not be the same person who leaves the hospital to go back to "the world." It is a new, impatient patient who recovery makes eager to pursue new hopes and expectations. Despite John Burroughs' resigned line, "Serene I fold my hands and wait," humans hate to wait, especially modern American humans. No, resignation is seldom learned in modern life, and rededication does well to make it out of the gate and around the first turn. When was the last time you kept a New Year's resolution past noon of the second day?

In view of surviving the test and throwing off the burden of that earlier apprehensiveness, I have grown lighthearted. Maybe I should have been more lighthearted; maybe that's what happened to me. I was too cynical, too busy finding flaws in the fabric rather than valuing the design. On the other hand, I despise people who talk continually of going through life smelling the roses and finding the silver lining of every dark cloud that appears in the blue.

On the other hand (part two), if the course of my life had not been radically altered by this heart transplant, I would have been dead in the prescribed course of life—if there had been a prescribed course of life. I don't think you come into the world with a blueprint of existence, just as I don't think that God is going to make an exception of the individual just because the individual wants that exception. I believe in God, I believe in prayer; my belief in prayer is personal, whether it is merely psychologically soothing or whether it's effective on a statistical basis. I don't know or care. It works with me, and to know that dozens of people were praying for me not only made me feel good, it sustained me in many down moments when I was not quite sure that life held any future or any more exciting times than I had already passed through.

There is that contrary human element of danger/comfort; the animal is uncomfortable with comfort. We fear it, don't we all, somewhere inside? Especially unearned or unlooked-for comfort— but who ever feels his comfort is unearned? I think it ironic that while we all can believe in the existence of evil in the world—a spiritual evil concentrated, perhaps, in what we call "the devil"—we find it hard to believe in good. Yet if we observe, we will find more examples of the latter than of the former. It is the blazing, penetrating quality of evil that seems to overwhelm us, whereas good, although prevalent, is not dangerous, is not stark and alarming, is not savagely attractive. It is a sort of daily presence that we say we *know* yet do not acknowledge. We take for granted, in the ordinary course of our day, that the car coming down the highway toward us is not going to hit us deliberately, that persons in tall buildings will not throw heavy objects down on us. (This is "good." But if somebody *does* throw something down on us, if they do hit us, is that "evil"?)

The philosophical side of a new heart seems to differ with age. I learned to think of myself first, not selfishly but to quit putting off for that future self that is so difficult to recognize—old age; to quit hoarding things like Christmas aftershave in anticipation of needing them worse later on. I need them now. I need *life* now. There is no "later on" for me. Or is this true of everybody, not just transplantees?

Many wonder if heart transplantees aren't haunted by the idea that someone had to die in order for them to live. While I am sure this nags at the edges of many of us, I know of no transplantee who feels the amount of guilt such a thought might imply. It has been said (and I agree) that this thought occurs primarily to people observing the transplant, not the recipient. When I was in the hospital—I really haven't thought much about it since then—the first day or two after I had come to from the operation, I thought, My God, I've got the heart of a man who, a week ago, didn't dream that not only would he be dead but his heart would be in somebody else. Delight in that wonderful new condition removes such thoughts after a few days or hours.

That unfortunate man who is now part of me couldn't have imagined such a translation of parts, and only a few years back I couldn't have imagined taking into my breast a foreign object, supposedly the center of life and love, and instantly making it my own center of existence. If that's fate, then it's a fate you have no control over once you are committed to survival. The transplant process is not something you choose or flip a coin over. There are other cardiac processes which, you might say, are by choice. Heart transplant boils down to once-always. There's no choice. Or if there is choice, it simply is the choice of existence or nonexistence. There are very, very few instances where someone was eligible (medically) for a heart, turned it down, and continued to survive with any kind of style. The wise transplantee, after his first, second, third year, still doesn't make long-range plans. It's too shattering, too nerve-racking. Why try to confine fate to a set of dates? There is only one future for any of us, transplantees or not, which is now.

There is no selfishness in the idea that the patient is glad to have received a new life, not weighing the fact it was at the cost of another life. That other life was already lost, so cost is really not the word for it. True, another person died, but there the connection ends. If anything, the successful transplantee thanks the vanished donor, possibly offering the assurance that it is wonderful just to be able to sleep on your side, to be able to breathe again and feel well throughout your system. That's what might be whispered if, for a few seconds, communication were possible. Gratitude without guilt is the only proper and healthy response to receiving a new heart.

Advice to would-be transplant patients: If you're going to talk to somebody, talk to somebody who's had the operation, who's *had* the transplant. Don't talk to someone who's observed, even intimately, who might have done overly much introspection or found some ethical or philosophical taint in the process. Don't talk guilty worries to a doctor or to your spouse or another close one. Talk worry and worried ideas to someone who's been through it, to someone who's had it done and survived. For the concerned, that can be more help than anything else.

Chapter 16

The idea of new heart, new start is not just some cute rhyme thought up for a public relations project. Nearly every successful heart transplantee I've encountered is not only able to transcend old emotions but is eager to do so. The *new start* begins with regaining of consciousness. You go beyond becoming an evangelist for the procedure, as Dr. Ring accused his little flock of doing, you become Columbus, finding a new world. Sure, like Columbus, you may think the inhabitants of your new world are one thing when in fact they are another, but the discovery is what is important, not who. Historians can draw conclusions as erroneous as anyone else, and historians say Columbus didn't benefit much from his discoveries and died a poor man. Indeed, with history does wealth become the only yardstick? Columbus found what he was seeking, and the satisfaction of the discovery must have made him one of the most successful figures in civilization's biography. Finding a new world for yourself may not be as everlasting as Columbus's discovery, but to the transplanted heart it has the same power of regeneration, the same power to redraw your life maps, to recharge your old Europes.

My first heart transplant anniversary sneaked up on me. All of a sudden there it was, just a few numbers away on the calendar. Part of this unexpectedness came from the way I felt physically, which was exceptionally fit. How could I have recovered so rapidly and so completely from the feeble, helpless animal I was only a year before? Shouldn't I still be observing restraints on my activities? Although I hadn't taken time to do much private prognostication during those first dozen months, I wouldn't have predicted such robustness under any circumstance.

Another part of unexpectedness issued from a number of events outside the transplant circle. New heart or old, life must go on, and fortunately my life *could* go on and at an unusually safe pace, considering the wear and tear on body, mind, and emotions. One should be gratified that life *can* go on as easily as it does although, again, this is the kind of defense that trauma sometimes triggers. For those who rely on the winds being tempered to convalescent lambs, forbear. Life does not stop or magically straighten itself out into a yellow brick road. The thorns still grow in the path, the chasms still yawn, the clouds still gather overhead to rain on whoever is under them. No, the changing life is within. You become a new person and, thankfully, most of those near and dear to you absorb some of that new life. My first year after transplant included personal tragedy, financial near-disaster, and a good bit of family alarm and strife—the sort of things that occur in any large family or to everyone who has had to spend months or years in some crippled condition. (No need for me to relate particular incidents because they are not that unusual: death and taxes, misunderstanding among siblings, blame sprinkled throughout both kin and acquaintances.) Life does go on in much the same way life goes on regardless of our attempts to make it less so. But that business of new heart, new start not only puts new spirit in your fighting back, it throws new light on your inspection of what is and what is not important. The successful transplantee learns, if nothing else, not to spend too much time on unimportant things, thoughts, or fears. And few things are truly important once you inspect them in that new light.

Approaching that first heart anniversary, the transplant office sent me a formidable listing of the tests and procedures that must be done: tests of the toenail-to-hairtip variety covering nearly three days:

- Complete eye examination, checking for diseases and visual acuity. The aftermath of heart transplantation can require several changes in lens prescriptions as well as balancing your medications; even then, visual satisfaction can't be assured. (Although my pill and capsule regimen didn't cause eye problems, after trying several lenses throughout the first year, I continued to get a headache around my left eye if I tried to read in bed.)
- Bone densitometry tests, using scanning methods that not only draw a direct color picture of hip and spine sections but electronically calculate the quality of bone structure. Here I also learned something new to me, that there are two kinds of bones: compact and spongy. The bones of the spine are spongy and flexible while the hip bones are compact and will generally thin with age or loss of calcium. However, all bones will continue to "remodel," ordinarily at lessening speed, through a complicated system of calcium exchange between bones and blood so that even the elderly are provided a continuous supply of new and reactive bone. (Most transplantees must take calcium supplements due to the effects certain medications have on the body's calcium "factory," although there is some question as to the supplements' effectiveness in comparison to a suitable intake of calcium-rich food and drink.)
- Biopsy, right and left heart, done in the cardiac cath lab. (Once during a local television show when I was describing the manner in which the bioptome is introduced into the heart, via the neck and veins, a camera operator fainted.) An arteriogram, preceded by a shot of Demerol and accompanied by a saline IV, is performed at the same session, the catheter usually introduced through a vein in the groin and worked upward to the heart, where dye is shot into the veins and observed by X ray as it illuminates the arteries of the heart. By the time these processes have looked at it or taken out bites, the heart is a well inspected organ and most rejection events can be predicted, if imminent, and prevented. As I noted earlier, neither the biopsy nor the arteriogram is very

painful, although lying on the narrow operating table that is used can become tiresome, and after the arteriogram the patient is required to go to bed with leg kept flat for six or so hours.

- An echocardiogram done in your bed (because of the need for rest after the arteriogram, I became an in-patient for one day and night), using high-frequency sound waves (silent ultrasound) to open a two-dimensional "window" of the heart—an easy process since the patient simply lies in bed while the technician smears a touch of gel on the chest, then poses the transducer (which emits and receives the sound waves and looks something like an old-fashioned telephone receiver) over the heart's location.

- Lab work, including extensive blood and urine testing as well as minute stool samples tested for occult blood, plus frequent taking of vital signs to monitor blood pressure and heart rates throughout the test period. Most blood lab work must be done after fasting—that is, no food or drink for the preceding ten or twelve hours. Heart transplant patients must have cyclosporine trough levels determined through special blood tests. Trough levels are the rate the medication is or is not being absorbed and retained, and indicate the size of dosage or a change in dosage upward or downward. If all goes well, the immunological medications will usually drop to minimum dosages and remain there after a year.

- Stress testing is done in the pulmonary lab to ascertain oxygen use and pulmonary functions. This involves some arterial blood collecting and a great deal of huffing and puffing into various kinds of pipes and conduits and (at one point) inside an air-tight glass compartment somewhat resembling an old type (circa 1970s) telephone booth. The stress test puts you walking the treadmill with a huff-puff tube in the mouth, testing the body's metabolic use of oxygen, an important function of the heart's blood circulation action.

- Chest X rays to compare sizes of the heart over the past twelve months and X rays of all joints and potential trouble spots. An EKG and a general physical exam are also done.

The physical exam includes checking the prostate gland on a man, proctoscopy, probing of neck and axillary glands, scalp and head examination, looking at nails to see if calcium deficiency is evident, and tickling the soles of the feet to test neural responses. (See, I told you it went from hair to toenails!)

- The U. T. Southwestern/St. Paul program also includes the Magnetic Resonance Imaging (MRI) test. Not all transplant programs do this, but since it seems to work rather effectively, I would predict that more and more facilities will employ the MRI if such a lab is available.

And yes, even this brief expedition in hospitalization can cost a shocking amount of money, but after a year the transplantee has either learned to live with shocking sums for all things medical or has found ways to accommodate or postpone them. So it is not unexpected. And the brighter side of the experience is that with satisfactory results, the heart transplantee will then be "free" for as long as six months or, with such procedures as the arteriogram, a year. In my case I continued seeing my cardiologist every three months for EKG, lab work, and a physical going-over. X rays are generally done on a six-month basis or according to what the cardiologist feels is needed. And by the end of a year most transplanted hearts will have achieved what I call environmental compliance; they will have expanded or reshaped themselves to fit the body's needs without becoming enlarged to a dangerous point.

Shortly after my first year following transplant, on orders of nurse Sarah and physiologist Lee at rehab, I took what is known as the Rockport Fitness Walking Test whereby you walk at a steady pace but as fast as you can do so comfortably, a timed, measured mile, then your pulse rate is taken immediately. (I warned Sarah, who is quite a beauty, that having her take my pulse might skew the results!) At the time I took the test the charts were based on weights of 170 pounds for men and 125 pounds for women. If you weigh substantially more, your relative cardiovascular fitness level will be slightly overestimated. If you weigh substantially less, your level will be slightly underestimated. Don't use this as a gauge of your own potential, but my first Rockport mile (as walkers call it) took me sixteen minutes and thirty-eight seconds, and my ending pulse rate was 130 beats per minute, which, for the male age group, put me smack in the middle of "average" on the charts that come with the test and form the real point of the tests. Of course, being a male, I immediately began demanding that I be retested, that I could do "better," competitiveness coming to the front even when competing with myself. (And I'll have you know that I surpassed that first Rockport test with my next timed mile which put me in the "above-average" segment of the fitness level chart.)

The heart rate you should strive to maintain while exercising is called the "target" heart rate (this is for all levels of exercise, not just cardiac rehabilitation). Your pulse rate (heartbeat) should be taken at the wrist. The target rate can be determined by subtracting your age from 220 and then multiplying the result by 70 percent. Your maximum rate is found by subtracting your age from 220—that's the highest pulse rate you should experience. The older you are the lower this maximum rate becomes. For example, I'm 65 and when that is subtracted from 220 it gives a maximum pulse rate of 155 beats per minute. Taking 70 percent of that 155 gives me a target rate of 108. (If I were thirty, both maximum and target rates would be considerably higher.) Most of the time, pulse rates and blood pressure are measured at peak and then at resting periods, and there is an intricate formula for determining things like "heart rate reserve" (subtract resting rate from maximum rate); "heart rate raise" (multiply heart rate reserve by .70); or add heart rate raise to resting heart rate and that will equal your target rate.

What these tests establish is the recommended composition of your exercise program. After every test the male or female fitness-walker (a jargonistic term getting more and more frequent use) is given a detailed chart for every phase of a walking program—color coded for those of us who tend to get lost in a numbers thicket. These time and distance figures (a twenty-week yellow program) are for me specifically, not my general age group. I was given actual minute times I should spend on warm-up (five to seven minutes per day);

mileage (two and a half miles to increase by the week to the twentieth week's plateau of four miles, which I think is unreal!); the pace or miles per hour (three to four and a half, or whatever is comfortable) that enables you to make your mileage numbers, also increasing to week twenty; what the ideal heart rate should be on finishing the mile (heart transplantees will always have a faster rate, as explained earlier); the length of cooldown time after exercise (five to seven minutes), and the frequency of your exercise period per week, with five times per week suggested for all categories, although it is explained that three times per week is sufficient. I'm going into some detail on this not because I'm pushing this particular test—which is prepared by the University of Massachusetts Medical School and sponsored by a shoe company—but because it forms the basis for lifetime fitness-walking programs. Once your "best effort" numbers are established you can stay with it for the rest of your life, or if you're younger, advance to a more frequent workout period or higher category as results indicate. Naturally, since the test is sponsored by a shoe company, a whole lot of walking is recommended for a whole lot of days per week, although I'm sure the test measurements were established before the sponsorship was. I am sure there are similar tests that achieve the same purposes, but I am more familiar with the Rockport, which is in widespread use, and in contrast to most medical/physical tests, is relatively easy to take and simple to interpret.

_____ Chapter 17

The most important event of my life happened to me while I was unconscious. I have been through and described the old agonies of waiting, hoping, stumbling; I have tried to tell convincingly of moving into the brighter day of a new heart, new start, new life, and I have now lived this new life long enough to believe I don't need to earn it, it is mine. But there is a continually deeper meaning to existence than that surface we drift, ride, or surf across. So what brought me here?

In writing this book I relied almost exclusively on the witnessing of others about the deepest beginnings of this new life. The witnesses are trustworthy, but no witness can rest a questing soul like the eyewitness. I had to describe this supreme moment of change from the outside even though I was the center of the drama. I almost had to think of it all as having happened to a third person. And yet, only after these years of freedom—freedom from medical questioning— could I go back to *see* and understand, for my readers and myself, the mechanics of a birth that became a nonmechanical rebirth. So, armed with new knowledge, new acceptance, and minus old fears and dreads, I have reconstructed the time and place where that most important event took place, the way it happened, the dramatis personae involved, with a trained, more reasoning curiosity.

When they first took me into the operating room, I was dazed but still awake. I had showered and been prepped, shaved across the chest, and virtually baptized with the brownish Betadine solution that cleanses the skin, making me a suitable platform for the coming production. I didn't realize it because of the many other medications I had had, but I had also been given my first dosage of cyclosporine to start the protection of my new heart (when I got it) from rejection. I was ready physically, emotionally, and mentally. I didn't know when they began draping me with sterile blankets, as they are called although not made of cloth. The effect of the anesthesia was almost immediate. I looked up for a single remembered second and thought I saw the sun, then the present disappeared; ten seconds and I was no longer there. Thus began a long period of ascribing vague and incorrect descriptions to badly remembered objects and poorly re-called recollections but that will remain forever in memory as "the day I got a new heart."

The human is an animal. That fact can never be erased from any life, and although we try to deny it and go to great lengths to cover it up, underneath, close to the bone, we are animals. We do what animals do. We think like animals once we close our eyes and let our minds drift. We like to be fed. We like to have our ears scratched. We like company. We run in packs. We hunt by packs. We live in tribes. We will find a tribe, artificial though it may be. We fit comfortably into each other. We are superior animals, we tell our-selves, because we can control our animalism, which of course is amusing and erroneous. An essence of mystery hangs over the whole process. I went to another land, a traveler in time and space, although both were present when I arrived back on earth.

The operating room: In most hospitals there are many, each for certain purposes. This is where miracles are performed as a matter of course, but here death also sits, observing, waiting, unseen but almost tangibly present, just beyond the penetration of the lights, hovering in the wings, waiting for a cue to come onstage at the first sign of error, weakness, or mischance, following a millimeter behind the scalpel blade from the moment it touches the surgeon's hand.

The OR strikes fear in most people, not only the patient. The patient seldom knows where he is by the time he enters it. The greatest fear is held by the concerned loved ones just outside the doors. If they speak at all it is in hushed, worried tones, regardless of the subject, as if unseen listeners were hovering over the gathering. The waiting room outside the OR is no place for levity and mirth. Only the morgue is more mysterious and more frightful than whatever takes place behind those closed doors.

There is no pronounced boundary to this world of the operating room, and yet there is a boundary that cannot be breached or lightly transgressed. One never enters on a lark. Surgery is a medical term hinting at expeditions into an unknown country, a challenge to spy out a territory as unpredictable to the surgeon as was the Great West to Lewis and Clark. Every operation, from the simplest to the most complex and time-consuming, has aspects of difference and discovery. As any experienced surgeon will vouch, once inside you never know what you will find. Hearts, which are the most stylized of all organs, assuming in our minds a shape that signifies everything from love to patriotism, are actually quite varied, not only in size but in placement. Some hearts grew in at a tilt, and some transplanted hearts may have slipped, either at the time they were transplanted or through some inscrutable internal inversion. Some people pose a real difficulty for biopsy or arteriogram performances because it is difficult to "get into" their hearts. Reliable maps to the individual human body can't be obtained from cartographers.

There is a feeling of drama when the overhead surgical spotlights are switched on, illuminating the stage where the operation will take place and leaving the rest of the room in semidarkness, the way the theater takes on its sudden, mystical aura when the house lights go down and the stage lighting takes over the audience's suspended comprehension. The stage is small, no bigger than the human chest. Whether the curtain is going up or coming down depends on which side of it you are on. It goes up for the group of masked individuals, it comes down for the unseen individual upon whom the play is about to be performed. The stage is small, but the drama is the biggest in the world. It is the battle between life and death. The curtains of anesthesia close in, and the final act begins, a reversal of literal theater procedure. Masked and faceless worshipers gather around the altar, uniformly clad in the paper suits called scrubs. The surgeons' heads are encased in close-fitting caps of cloth, with wide masks across nose, mouth, and chin; on their foreheads, fitted like helmets, are small microphones, and a recording video camera is also attached to the leader's head, making it possible to review the operation and, like a football coach watching films of last Sunday's game, gather his team around to point out procedures that might be done differently.

A modern operating room is always cold. The human mind and hand seem to work best several degrees cooler than room temperature. Most operating rooms have no outside windows. The OR is a world that must spin along disregarding what is taking place beyond and outside it. And it is definitely not the setting in which one expects to behold miracles. It's too sterile looking, too jumbled, uninspiring. But even without the lights and the participants, without the sounds of the machines (each sound whispering volumes to ears trained to listen and act on the gauges' advice), it is dramatic, as galvanizing to the alert imagination as any breathtaking laboratory scene on film. Along with the institutional greens or tans, rather rapidly a different color can and will be added to the scene when the chest is opened and removal of the organs is begun, and some artery may suddenly give a pop and spray color all over the cast; it is not uncommon for the surgical team to end a transplant session with their shoes full of it. Red. Blood. The most powerful color the human race is heir to.

The drama is ready to start.

Midnight: The surgery charge nurse, in scrubs, her long hair closely bound in a plastic snood, mask in place over her face—but the eyes showing those unmistakable signs of femaleness—enters the OR to say the procurement team has phoned, the donor heart has been removed and will be arriving at St. Paul after a drive of some seven miles in ten minutes.

12:48 A.M.: The surgery charge nurse announces, with excitement in her voice, that the retrieval team has arrived downstairs, and the new heart is on its way to the operating room. When Ring enters the room, many persons—mostly doctors—are waiting to watch his every move. Seconds later two men in fresh scrubs enter the room, followed by the nurse from the organ bank. She carries the beer cooler to a table, opens it, and asks one of the surgical team, "How

would you like it?" Through his mask he asks her to remove the
container and the heart from the ice chest. She takes out a saline-
filled plastic bag from the cooler, puts the bag on a table, and slowly
unwraps a smaller plastic container, exposing the clear cylinder. This
is the first view the OR has of the new heart.

1 A.M.: The green-tiled OR is like a laboratory; around the large
room are shelves of odd and unusual things, and spread out on
tables—lying at hand, sterile and ready—are all kinds of materials
that may or may not be called for during the operation. A war room
whose monitors are watched with the intensity of a command post
tracking a missile. A team of three anesthesiologists stands at the
head of the operating table, watching their machines and reading the
patient's vital signs. The array of wires, knobs, green and red lights,
pipes, and tubing seems nothing but a jumble, but the slightest
murmur of the machine and a hand reaches out to turn a knob and
a voice suggests, softly but distinctly, that someone at the table do
this or cease that. In the OR, all-nighters are almost routine, one day
blending into the next.

1:05 A.M.: The room and the actors in it are calm as the play
begins. Only if that dark, disliked spectator Death heckles, threatens
to march on and upstage everyone, will there be a flurry, the outcries
and excitement so dear to the imagined world of silver screen and
video tube.

Two surgeons and their backups begin opening the chest to receive the donor heart. As head of the team, Dr. Ring orchestrates
the procedure. It is routine work, and some member of the team asks
if music would be okay. Ring says yes but then complains about the
country-western music on the radio. He prefers rock and roll; he gets
rock and roll.

Even as we watch we sense we are witnessing something otherworldly, that forces of life and death are battling somewhere at the
edge of existence. A battle that involves more than the continuation
of the person under the bloodstained surgical blanket; the continuation of everyone in the room. Even the observers not taking part in
the work can feel it: The surgical team is fighting for all of us,
showing us one more time how lucky we are that miracles can be
performed instead of visiting haphazardly.

Transplant surgical teamwork is highly dependent on the emphasis of that first part of that word: *team*. Every move must be automatic, must be swift—in and out quickly, without undue hesitation or perplexity. Nurses have equal status within the team because titles are meaningless in the OR, just as the celebrity quarterback can't function without the untouted line. The associates, who can be respected surgeons in their own right, must be able to move with a kind of balletic grace when swift, sure moves are demanded. It is not at all unusual for the head surgeon on one operation to assist on another, and now that successful transplantation has been practiced in the OR for two decades, more and more associates will leave to take over new transplant programs of their own.

Although we have all seen movies where the put-upon surgeon in charge has to yell and demand and scream imprecations at some bumbling staffer, in the real, daily OR that kind of behavior is neither tolerated nor necessary. The surgeon in charge can and does get a biting demand in his voice from time to time, and tempers easily run over the top during a lengthy operation—and some transplant operations can run thirteen to twenty-four hours—but the responses come not through fear but through routine. Everyone knows what to do next even when "next" has not happened before. As for exclamations of irritation, once the operation's over they're left in the OR along with the bloody drapes, the filled basins, the tubes and tanks.

Despite my sounding a touch too mystical in saying it, there is unquestionably a kind of brotherhood among surgeons (or sisterhood, as more and more female surgeons are working in transplant programs) that gives them an understanding of certain arcane personal views and emotions. Surgeons are very sure of things in and out of the OR. Other M.D.s tend to dislike surgeons or mistrust them, not on a personal basis so much as for their primary instinct: They like to cut. And to a doctor who does not cut, it's a sign of the ego-compulsive single-mindedness that drives them. A surgeon probably works harder and longer and happier (in working so long) than any other medical professional with a choice. And at that, plenty of the better-known transplant surgeons go pretty near that long when working on a complicated procedure. Does this make the surgeon sound heartless, dedicated to his craft but not his patient? That is not the intention, and I will stand as witness that it isn't always the case, but the tendency of other health professionals to make a god of the chief surgeon is so strong that the air of being medically aloof, to the sacrifice of common emotion, is undeniable.

In the OR, worldwide reputations are gained and, on rare occasions, lost. Here medical news is made swiftly, often in an instant. "He lives!" is the ultimate triumph in medicine. We read about these heroic, lengthy operations where life is dramatically shifted from the newly dead to the barely living; with a warm, still-beating but faulty heart ripped out and replaced by a new, cold and efficient organ; the first gush of blood going through the chilled heart, the few seconds that stretch into hours—or into an eternity—as the surgical team waits; then, if the heart starts moving, the liver pinks up, the lungs deflate, inflate, comes the words of relief: "That's it" or "It's going to work." That is the great moment of truth that momentarily overwhelms even the most sophisticated transplant surgical team, when life returns to what has been essentially a passively dead body, when the red glow of life infuses an organ, when the heart makes stuttering and then suddenly speedy steps toward regaining something that has been held in suspension for hours, right to the verge of extinction. It surges back and becomes once more what it had been: a healthy, beating powerhouse of life.

Is it any wonder, then, that surgeons are the most egotistical, most arrogant and brash members of the medical profession? Self-belief is as imperative as instruments in their trade. Every incision, every final suture is a challenge. It is said that transplant pioneers clung doggedly to the notion that the success of the process lay solely in the hands of the surgeon. Denton Cooley's 1968 prescription for heart transplanting was "cut well, tie well, get well." It still holds a philosophical attraction for the surgeon, even when he recognizes that such is not the case, even while he shrugs off the operation as a simple cutting maneuver.

Surgeons say the thrill of victory over death is the most energetic, most exhausting, but the most satisfactory passion in all medicine. It is not unlike birth—new birth, rebirth, resurrection—but it is more thrilling even than the birth of a baby because it keeps going a human narrative that began only as an unpredictable story with a baby's arrival. But in this OR a life that has been destroyed is salvaged so that a new life can be created, and what comes from under the knife (to resort to that timeless cliché) and emerges through the anesthetic is new, regardless of how many years its housing has been on earth.

1:08 A.M.: Ring moves quickly to stand over the unconscious patient whose chest has been opened by another surgeon. (For the next few hours Ring will scarcely move a step.) The surgical instruments used sound like the lineup in an old-fashioned butcher shop: knives, saws, hooks, expanders, and retractors (or good old rib-spreaders). The bone saw, which is used to open the patient's chest by cutting through bone and cartilage at the sternum, is an electrical appliance that looks pretty much like the home workman's hand-held circular saw. In use, the bone saw can follow a very delicate pattern, coming within millimeters of sensitive organs without injuring them.

The rib-spreader spreads the ribs so that the heart can be exposed. Most people do not realize the lower front ribs are more cartilage than bone so that they spread easily, and if ribs are broken by the rib spreader during open heart surgery, it will be the back ribs, which can break from the pressure or compression put on them. I am assured this is rare, however, and usually involves some abnormality in the frame of whoever is undergoing the operation. In my own case I did not suffer any soreness or uncomfortableness from the ribs following my heart transplant. One reason I may not have is that I was quite slender—let's say "skinny"—and there was very little excess girth to squeeze against my back ribs. I seem to be fascinated by the rib-spreader even though I view it as looking like a medieval torture implement. It's so down to earth, and there's little enough of that in our modern world, but I'm sure someone has already improved on the hand-cranked model, adding some electric or electronic aspect to this contrivance.

The ugly, scary first act has taken place: The first pencil-line slice of the scalpel has been made, then the firestick (an electric knife) has been applied to slice quickly through the skin, the fat, and the muscle; a wisp of smoke and the aroma of singed flesh, frequently sizzling with a noise that falls alarmingly on the unaccustomed ear but cauterizing the open wound so that there is only a slight amount of blood, the surgeons moving in hurried rhythm to clamp and tie the larger bleeders although dozens of tiny spots of blood can challenge the surgeon with their unscheduled eruption. Then comes the whine of the bone saw cutting through the hush of the room. The bone wax is applied and the rib-spreader is slowly but steadily ratcheted so that the human armor plate of cartilage is pushed back, exposing the ugly, dying heart that must be removed swiftly and discarded.

Nearly everyone who observes an operation cringes at some point in the process. It can come from the sight of so much blood or the sounds and smells given off during stages of entrance. The bone saw, in particular, puts the hair on end in an open heart or thoracic operation. The idea that bones can be sawed in two without ruining them forever is foreign to our minds. The smell of scorched human flesh arouses something primordial in us: We don't have to be told what that shocking odor is as the firestick singes its way through layers of skin and fat. Some reactions are instinctive and can be overcome only with the training surgical teams go through. Such as? Such as the chill bumps that appear when you realize that *is* a staple gun and yes, it *is* shooting steel staples into that person's chest. Such as the bone-chilling feeling we get when we know that a piece of aseptic stainless steel screamed while biting its way into something solidly human—fingernails screech across the blackboard of our nerves. No one, hearing it for the first time, can grasp the importance of the suctioning; it sounds grossly terrifying. And we react emotionally anytime we observe another human helpless, tied down, but open to the whims of some fate. How apt is T. S. Eliot's simile, "The evening is spread out against the sky like a patient etherized upon a table."

Blood panics even the sturdiest person if he's not prepared for it. During World War II, I served as a Navy corpsman with the Marines, and I observed how hardened combat riflemen who had gone through such hells as Guadalcanal, the landing on Tarawa, or Iwo Jima would sometimes waver on their feet at the sight of blood from a cut on their thumb, and these were men who had sighted across the tip of an M1 rifle or held down the barrel of a Browning automatic rifle and unhesitatingly pulled a deathly trigger. Yet I, who had been trained to ignore blood as something to be sponged away or stanched, would probably have gotten buck fever when I perceived a human target open, big, and condemned to die if I made a tiny movement with one deadly finger.

Second act: Ring and an assistant connect the patient to the heart-lung (or bypass) machine, which takes over its functions once the heart has been stopped or removed. Patients are *ventilated* when they must be put on the breathing machine (ventilator) to help the lungs and are *intubated* when they are stuck full of siphons, tubes, and such. What happens when the tubes are pulled out? They are *disintubated.* (Being what Robert MacNeil called *wordstruck,* I felt a compulsion to establish *antidisintubatedmentarianism* as part of hospital nomenclature, my definition being: opposition to the tightly held, medically schismatic belief that taking tubes out of the victim makes him feel better. The nurses privately agreed to humor me because I was out of my head, and the more I argued, the solider their conviction grew.)

The surgeons pull back for a few seconds to see that the machine is performing well. It seems to be. Someone signals to one of the bank of monitors, safe so far. The invention of this machine is what made today's open-heart surgery possible. It was developed by Dr. John H. Gibbon, Jr., who first successfully used the evolved machine on a human in a cardiopulmonary capacity in May 1953. Earlier work on artery suturing and transplantation experiments had been done by French Nobel prizewinner Alexis Carrel, and in 1936 America's "Lone Eagle," Charles A. Lindbergh, worked with Dr. Carrel on experiments that led Carrel to develop the so-called Lindbergh heart, an artificial heart device. Lindbergh was joint author with Carrel on a pioneering volume, *The Culture of Organs,* in 1938. The Lindbergh heart was a predecessor of Dr. Gibbon's heart-lung machine on which the latter began working early in the 1940s. The length of time that a patient can stay on the bypass machine has increased to the point that it is now a matter of hours, not minutes. I am told I was on bypass for a rather lengthy period, but whatever the time might have been, there apparently were no sad effects.

The old, diseased heart is severed from its lifelong ties; four major cuts release the arteries that connect it to the lungs and the rest of the body. The old heart is lifted out, dripping, passed from one gloved hand to another. A basin is produced, and the worthless organ is dumped, possibly to twitch for a few seconds or maybe not at all. It is the end of something that began so many years before, something that was considered irreplaceable. The bypass machine takes up the circulatory system; the body under the knife is motionless except for the in-and-out action of the machine. Death takes a step closer to the stage, sensing its opportunity to enter the drama.

1:30 A.M.: As the work proceeds, team members call out questions or suggestions to one another. With some nod or perhaps instinct, the other members react without further explanation: It is a precision apparatus, this surgical team, each part doing its specific task, progressing toward a common goal.

The clock moves, but how can we pronounce it slow or swift? The intensity is such that no clock can record anything as important as what we are seeing and feeling. Time has had a stop. Seconds have become hours, hours days, and days merge into ages.

2 A.M.: The new heart, taken from its cylinder where it has been kept, is handled carefully but without hesitation. It is lowered into the chest hole where the old heart resided for so many years and partially sutured into place. In the OR the sutures go around, connecting arterial ends, the way you sew a cuff rather than the way you stitch two pieces of cloth together. The tension in the room among the team members is almost palpable now. No one is looking away, gazing purposelessly; hands, eyes, and minds are vigilant. Ring stares at a monitor, his concerns and fears, if they are there, hidden behind the mask that reveals only his eyes. He announces slowly, reluctantly: "We're going to have to sit for a while on bypass." The new heart is acting sluggish, refusing to take up the load it must carry quickly if the patient is to be restored. After an undetermined, interminable passage of minutes that could be hours, the once crowded room is emptied of everyone but the team, the technicians, and two observers.

"You didn't want to cancel your case tomorrow, did you?" asks the heart-lung machine operator, scheduled to work again with Ring in surgery at 8 A.M. Without taking his eyes from the monitor, Ring says sharply, "No!"

Mostly our idea of the OR is that the atmosphere is tense, the workers as taut and excited as rock climbers approaching the crest. Sometimes and at some point in any operation this is true. (I lived through a "simple" appendectomy that became highly stressful because it went on for four hours. "His damn appendix was wrapped around his backbone," the surgeon told my wife.) But most of the time in the OR an almost informal air prevails, a clublike atmosphere. Orders are more often given as questions, suggestions that are the more ironclad because they're *not* screamed or cursed. Especially in a long, difficult transplant operation, there is conversation, often on topics outside the arena, and some surgeons like music piped into the room. Some associates come and go, to relax, to get a cup of coffee, to think about something else for just a minute or maybe to rest their feet. But in the OR the importance of innate traits comes forth. A good surgeon has one asset that seems to be the tag that prices them all: concentration. The recognition of inborn talent we must give to a good surgeon is his ability to think in one straight line, paying no attention to what is happening outside his thoughts, outside his intense delving, literally, into the problem. The surgeon becomes almost a part of the body he is working on. Things outside that small, sensual ring do not intrude, scarcely exist, for him. That's why stories abound from every war of the surgeon's intensity while bombs fall, while bullets fly, while fires rage, while oceans threaten to wash away the whole ship. The surgeon is looking into a more eternal problem: the life of someone at his fingertips, someone, in many cases, he doesn't know about, has never seen before. I had a surgeon tell me he thought he actually glimpsed some metaphysical essence that is life itself, flashing (my presumption) beneath the blade or among the boiling blood, trying to escape or to survive. "Sometimes I can almost put my finger on it, can almost hold it with a forceps until the next crucial step is completed." The problem itself is what interests him, what keeps him riveted to his task. It is a deadly serious game; you win (life) or you lose (death). As stated, there are no ties. What is it, what can he do about it? Can he apply what he knows? Must he learn from this experience and apply something new, something terribly important, terribly immediate, potentially tragic?

Tragedy, of course, is always possible. There's no such thing as "good health" in an OR, only the hope of health, only the hope of future. There is *now*, there is no *then;* there is no "back when" or "in the future." The English language, as adaptable as it has been to scientific change and advancement, has a peculiarly narrow range when it comes to time. "Then" is indecisive—it goes either way, past and future, back and forth—*now* and then, *then* and now. But all these come together in the OR into a little shining dot that dances along with the scalpel, the retractor, the hemostat, the perfusionist's movements. The faces are masked; the face of the patient has disappeared beneath the blue cloth. There's a field of play; there are no people involved. People disappear once they come through the door of the OR, walking or pushed on a gurney.

Once, filming a particularly intensive operation while with a Navy film crew, I was holding a light reflector on the action. At a signal from the cameraman I moved in a bit too close to the theater of operation, and without even glancing up, without really knowing who or what was disturbing that sixth sense of rightness, the surgeon flipped a scalpel at me, missing me by a few centimeters. I know he wasn't angry or being personal. He had no idea who was creating that disturbance of his field of concentration, but disturbance it was, and his flip was automatic, unaimed, and without malice. I can forgive him now, but I'll admit at the time it upset me. And for the record, the picture we made that day—I was not the major cameraman by any means—was used for years by the Navy medical corps. It was an experimental operation, attempting to replace damaged spinal vertebrae with bone portions from the tibia (the larger of the two bones between our knee and ankle). The film was titled *Tibial Resection,* and several Navy doctors told me later they had seen it. I'm not sure how successful the procedure itself was or whether surgeons continued doing tibial resections, but I'm proud to have had a hand in making it. It introduced me to the OR and its mysteries, credits enough in a life.

Dr. Starzl, in Lee Gutkind's book *Many Sleepless Nights,* made an unusual confession for a surgeon or any other professional. He admitted he was not as good at surgery as when he was younger. "It would be nice to be young again," he said, "because the fact is, I was able to do better operations fifteen to twenty years ago than I am able today. I was a better surgeon then; I had better eyesight, more strength, undoubtedly better coordination." Starzl is probably the last of his generation's transplant gods, and despite some criticism of his often startling explorations of untested transplant frontiers, Gutkind feels he "towers like a tree in the transplant world." He adds, "There are other trees, such as Shumway, Cooley, Barnard, but no tree stands taller than Starzl."

3:30 A.M.: Finally Ring announces, "The new heart looks real good." The new heart is now functioning. He begins removing the tubes connecting the patient to the bypass machine. As the clamps are removed and the chest is moved back into place, the surgeons begin to wire the breastbone back together. With stainless steel staples one reconnects the breastbone (the sternum, which had been opened with the electric bonesaw), and Ring steps away from the table, letting associates close the chest and apply layers of paper tape and bandages. Ring oversees the job and says brightly, "Well, thanks, everybody. Time we can go home. Sorry I kept you up so late." An assisting surgeon laughs and whispers to another, "If he could figure out a way not to sleep and just operate all the time, he'd do it. He loves it."

Outside the OR, Ring unties the top of his mask, letting it dangle in front of him. The surgery coordinator hands him a Diet Coke, and Ring steps over to a table so he can write orders for medication and treatment of the patient. Then he goes to the OR waiting room where the wife and family of the person on the OR table have stayed. He lets them know the transplant went well and their husband and father will shortly be removed to the Intensive Care Unit where he'll begin the recovery process. "It was a textbook case," he assures the family. "Couldn't have gone better."

Shortly before 4 A.M. Ring slumps in a chair in the ICU where the newly transplanted person has been taken. Ring is eating a sandwich on white bread that someone has handed him, remarking that it may not be completely "heart healthy" but it's something to take the edge off working for twelve hours or more without a bite of food. After the sandwich (which he looks at quizzically before eating the rest of it), he goes back into the ICU to take a look. "I just have to check the patient one more time," he tells one of the assistants. When he leaves a short time later, he knows that within a shockingly short time he'll return for another open-heart operation, then return to ICU to see how the patient is doing.

Denise Ring, his wife, shares some of the feelings that accompany the families of most surgeons. "The key to living with a transplant surgeon," she says, "is to know that they're unreliable and unpredictable. You don't get your expectations too high so you don't get disappointed by anything. And you're always happy with him for his patients who are receiving the new hearts. He's certainly not above feeling."

At the same time, like other medical wives, she wonders about the eventual toll of this life of virtually no "off-call" days on her husband: "We all worry about it—that all of a sudden he'll have missed a lot of his life because he was too busy in medicine."

Ring shrugs off such worries: "There are frequently days like this," he admits, but with a kind of relish. One suspects they are his favorite kind.

"That was the astonishing emotional thing about it. We went in and saw you, with all those machines, and that was really stunning, like the machines were alive and you weren't," Paul Duke, Jr., told me, speaking of that first morning as I was lying in ICU helpless but having passed through the operation.

"You hear about all the technology of medicine, but it didn't strike me until I saw you there. And the machines were panting and blinking, with readouts and all that kind of thing, and you, of course, were there, and your chest was going up and down—but it was automatic motion, and you weren't conscious; the machines were conscious for you. And you were kind of quivering, like a part of the machine, not living, just reacting.

"And then what we really saw, progressively, visiting day after day for a week or two, was that the machines would slowly disappear. We'd come in and there'd be two less machines, two less wires, and two less catheters. And the human being became more and more alive."

You look at the machines and see the lights, see the green, jagged lines going up and down, the balls of light going across the monitor screens. You hear the thump, the beat, and realize for the first time, "That's me, that's me doing that. Those are not machines, those lines and dots of light—those are *me*. That's my life. That's the measurement of where I am at this very moment. Not where I will be but where I am, that I am existing. That *is* my existence. That's evidence that I am alive."

And suddenly the enormous beauty of life itself, of being alive, overwhelms you, restores you, reinvigorates you, infuses you. For an uncounted moment you were a man with no heart, dead in every way but the unfathomable spirit. Now you are a person again, a being, a survivor.

As John le Carré put it, you are living against the odds.

Epilogue

Judge not the play before the play is done:
Her plot hath many changes; every day
Speaks a new scene; the last act crowns the play.
—*Francis Quarles*

Now the road begins to straighten out, I can see ahead for the first time. The hills are less pronounced, the map shows no dark valleys through which I dread to walk. I can look back now and not be afraid of what I see because it no longer pursues me into the future. I have passed several mileposts with their predicted terrors, and I have not had to experience them.

You ask, "You are normal, then?" and what can I answer but with another question: When was I ever normal? What is normal when you have a human life in mind as you ask? No, I am not normal. Very few of us carry around someone else's heart as I do. The definition of normal is "conforming to a type, standard, or regular pattern." So, if nothing else, I don't conform to a regular pattern. But I'm not abnormal, either, because that connotes strangeness or deformity, and as long as I keep my shirt on (literally), I display no signs of my peculiar condition. So I suppose I will settle for *atypical.* That I am . . . that *we* are.

So, some reader will ask with enough disbelief implied in the question to indicate its doubt, you are perfectly well now, have regained more than you lost, suffer no pains and have no regrets, are a new person, without stain or blemish? The answer to each part and to that whole train of thought is no. No, I am not perfectly well and never will be. No transplanted person is perfectly well any more than a piece of shattered crystal is perfect again even when it has been carefully and invisibly repaired.

For thousands of years we have spoken of breaking hearts and of stealing hearts, and sung songs about the sadness, the joys, and the dangers of giving our hearts away. "Give crowns and pounds and guineas/But not your heart away," Mr. Housman and his Shropshire lad warn us. The Mayan priests, atop their pyramids, sacrificed their victim by plunging an obsidian knife into his chest to rip out the still-beating heart to display to the worshipers; hearts mean bravery, strength, life, love, persona, the most valuable part of the human. (I have wondered why Salome, after her dance, asked her pleased uncle for the head of John the Baptist. Why didn't she ask for his heart? It seems to me that a woman would more instinctively prefer the heart, even a dying heart, to a grisly severed head. But then, that biblical account wasn't written by a woman, and Salome, to give her credit, was only following the demands of her mother.)

None of those immortals had me in mind when they gave all those sighs, sang all those songs, and made those poetic warnings. No, despite my prior protestations, I am not normal as history has defined physical normality. But I am beyond pondering the thought. Trying to be normal is a fruitless human exercise at best, and even more frustrating for the transplantee who must observe so many rules the normal person can disregard, who must plan his day around medication points, who can't plunge into some of life's refreshing pools but must sit on the bank. What would happen if you didn't take your medicine or if you missed taking it for a day or two? I don't know. I hope I never find out because I don't plan to miss it. I don't plan to *not* take it. Taking it doesn't bother me, it's *not* taking it I'm scared of.

Someone says, "You'll be doing this the rest of your life. You'll *have* to do this the rest of your life!" So what? We all have to do some things the rest of our life. (Is it indelicate of me to mention that every day we perform a number of bodily functions for which there is no hiring?) I'll eat two, three times a day, shave (voluntarily) three, five, seven times a week, brush my teeth, wash my hair, shower, find a clean shirt. Think of all the things I'll be doing the rest of my life. Nobody's going to do them for me. I'll be taking medicine the rest of my life? At least there is the rest of my life.

I am looking across a lake in winter. What brought me here was a skein of ducks sweeping down and landing with scarcely a ripple on the cold water. I saw them as I drove on the highway that crosses the dam, and I could not remove the memory of their flight from my wondering heart, so I returned.

I came asking about eternal things, timeless existence. Clutching my breast, I feel the beating heart that has been in me for two years—a moment, as time goes. I want to stretch my horizons of expectation if there is any stretch to them. Why would a flight of ducks make me think such thoughts? Well, the ducks headed straight in, they did not circle. They knew the exact patch of water they wanted in a bay that, to my unducklike gaze, looked the same as the rest of the lake. Something timeless guided them, something possibly eternal, because they were in passage.

I glance down the lake, seeing blue land rise at the far end of the water, an unknown shore. And the thought comes to me that as the ducks took to the waves in an everlasting pattern, so a distant shore is eternal, unchanging. Again, our Shropshire friend declares, "Earth and high heaven are fixed of old and founded strong."

I tell myself, Don't just watch the wildfowl; consider the eternal action of the water, gaze at the far shore, and try to decipher if any part of us lives unchanged, eternal as the flight of ducks, as the wavingly design of lake waters, as the blue magnetism of unexplored shores.

Eternal. There is that fear in all of us that there is no such thing, that we are the last of the tribe, the end of the line. *Après moi le déluge.* I ask myself (one has to be alone to dare it), "Will some of me live on?"

I must have spoken aloud because suddenly beside me on this shore a tinplate philosopher sits mocking. "Let's see if we can get this straight," he says. "You don't know how long you're going to live. Never have. You think you've got a new life, and *maybe,* because it's new, it's eternal. You know damn well it isn't, but it's new. So what else is new?"

I owe my life to many people and many events, but I recognize the debt, starting with parents and a grandmother who refused to let a newborn grandson die. And I must keep adding names, known and unknown, the tentmates, the cannon-mates, the truck-and-bunk-mates of war with whom I mixed salvations time after time, and that recent medical front line of cardiologists, surgeons, nurses, anesthesiologists. Or the last automobile driver I met, coming toward me, who in a matter of inches could (but didn't) abruptly end my life.

Yes, I know that far shore will undoubtedly yield disappointment: ratty houses, decrepit boat docks, flotsam of the American lake culture. And the baywater, dancing and eternal, is probably dangerous to human consumption. Even the ducks may be tainted by having partaken of some substance that, sooner or later, will eliminate the species.

But eternal things are what I seek, the way water laps and waves, and will keep on lapping, the infinite blueness of an imagined shore, the certainty that flights of ducks will drop cleanly and beautifully onto chosen waters. These have not changed since creation. Eternal is for how long? Even as I sit and muse on the thought, I glance up to see the flashing silver of another kind of bird, a bird of artifice whose passage is marked by sound but not by nature. That metal bird is me. I am not natural. I am manufactured. I love the natural world, but I'm no longer part of it. Have any of us been, once off our mother's breast? How new is eternity? How old is time?

It is easy to accept tinplate philosophy, and I accuse myself of doing that, trying to elicit an eternity that I hope to bring into my net. And I stare at my heart. The scar tells me a human heart is transitory, not eternal. Where is an eternal instinct that can bring me safely to my destiny? Are there eternities in the tides of life, the blowing, white-topped wavelets of our lakes and oceans?

Can I accept any definition of eternal but my own? The tinplate philosopher is a rugged individualist, never wrong to himself. Yes, I am acting silly, here on a day that is, at best, coldly uncomfortable, looking across a man-made lake into an imagined distance that I can reach in ten minutes, waiting for birds that fly to where man overcomes their ancient instinct to forage for themselves—and cages them with something stronger than wire: dependency.

I am being foolish, but I am probing existence. Have I been given a new life or merely an extension of an old life? What I call "my heart" may have been that of almost anyone. Its previous existence in another owner constitutes, for me, a blue distance, unexplored by choice, the impulse to explore pushed away by protective instincts as strong as any that shield the ducks. A new life? Perhaps. Continuation of an old life? My *no!* is determined . . . but unsure.

A new life. How shall I interpret that? Human instinct, unlike the instinct of a skein of ducks, cannot be trusted to land me safely on the waters of my man-made life. Earth and high heaven may be fixed of old and founded strong, but just a few days ago so was my heart. I am living proof that that verity is no longer veritable. New heart, new start? At what? At dependency, that wire cage. At change, that key to an unknown lock.

Eternal. There is the fear in all of us that there's no such thing, fear that rides the shoulder of everyone passing through the valley of the shadow. The transplantee doesn't make plans.

The tinplate philosopher ruminates, looks down at his feet, glances up through his eyelashes, and winks dramatically. For a while we sit and muse, wonder which is more important: man's survival or the art that accomplishes it? Man above process, or vice versa? Am I the leaf, the blossom, or the bole?

The tinplate philosopher says he's trying to figure out if I'm doing anything but romanticizing. He tries to make me recall the things I've learned, but the chart overflows; too much for one small head to carry.

"There is no death, what seems so is transition."

Now there's an eternal idea, there's a verity that no one can verify. The tinplate philosopher does not argue with the beauty of those words, but he shakes his head knowingly (a characteristic of tinplate philosophers) and declares that men fear death before they can spell the word. (Age five, on my father's shoulder, looking down into the open casket wherein lay an uncle, face unfamiliar, almost unknown to me, but then tears of realization I still feel, decades gone.)

So you escaped death, but you aren't free of that primordial fear, that first, worst recognition that there may *not* be something else.

You can't go back. The old life acquired, this one must slough off. What if the new, young heart becomes an alien, refuses to join the rest of me? When we think of years to come, what are we thinking of? Numbers? Growth? Purpose? My days of numbering are successfully submerged; why dream of growth if you are as fully grown as you are able to be? And is some new purpose, different from old purposes, demanded of me? One cannot go back and pick up any of it. New thoughts are filtered through a new heart.

The surgeons know (because they've been there) there's nothing to a heart but muscle—pumping, receiving, returning. They know its mystique is not contained in some arcane chamber unrevealed by the scalpel. There's no "black box" among the wreckage to explain the death of the heart, only the death of a muscle.

Starting over again, but where and how. I sit on a lonely shore and, well past the age of change, must change. Long past wanting to make decisions, I must make enormous decisions. Are we eternal? The ducks and geese, homing on polluted waters, may die by their own instinct. How should I, surrendering eons ago the right to live by instinct, figure out eternity? Why should a new heart involve so much hemming and hawing, so much attempting to decide about things that can't decide for themselves? My new start—is it at the beginning or am I merely resuming the race after falling behind on a far curve? Is there time to catch up?

Betty, my wife of thirty-nine years, died as I was finishing this book. She died of something for which medical science has no explanation and no preventive or cure. She had an easy death, however, if there is such a thing, and I was talking to her (hoping she was hearing) when her life ended beneath my fingertips. In light of that—her death and the inability of anyone to reverse the dying—do I still presume to offer what may seem to be excessively optimistic views of human terminality? I do. Her death changed nothing of what I believe as I have translated it onto these pages. She lived through the whole thing with me, she knew how I felt, what I hoped and whether or not I believed what I said I believed, and she agreed.

I try to tell the tinplate philosopher, you *can* begin again, you can catch up. That's too simple, he argues back. There must be a more complicated, more esoteric and compelling argument, either to rebut time or to waive it. Having survived through a miracle, a man wants to think he is miraculous. Ah, but a new argument occurs to me: Time returns. I have been given more time, or at least, with Joshua, can command, "Sun, stand thou still."

Nonsense, he sneers. Time is not lost or stopped. Time is lent. What you do with it is the question, not how much you have. Yes, but time has been regained for me, extended, but more than that, the clock has been reset many times, by chance or opportunity. Is time a shape around us? How long does it stretch? When does it end? The tinplate philosopher, taking advantage of my flight into fantasy, reminds me that in the case of my heart, the clock's hands can never again be depended on. Wrong once, resetting them adds only momentary integrity. Is there a finite definition of time? If there is an infinity, then time has no meaning. My new life can only be counted in moments. If I've regained time, it's only a little more, and that's no eternity. Who can guess the end of the sand in my hourglass or know how the next beam will fall on my sundial?

Before I go (and I grow colder as well as older) perhaps another flight, drifting down gracefully, will turn to me and honk an answer, knowing I can understand things now that I could not a little while ago. Maybe another skein will desoar upon the waters, will beckon me to observe, will induct in me the ability to understand the sky and the waters as they do. Time, their compass, is carried in their hearts, and surely ducks and geese, like mortal men, have hearts that do more than merely pump and pound and propel lifeblood?

But not another flight drops into that patch of water where my gaze falls. The day grows toward night. The blue distance becomes black. The waves decline to speak any language I can translate. It is answer enough for me.

The tinplate philosopher, waiting for better answers, still sitting on the shore, can be sensed if not seen as I drive away.

As for me, I am almost afraid to admit how good I feel, how successful my new heart has been. In fact, I no longer think of it as "my new heart."

It is simply . . . my heart.

Index

About the Author

A. C. Greene is an author and historian living in Dallas, Texas. A Fellow of the Texas Institute of Letters and the Texas State Historical Association, he is Coordinating Director of the Center for Texas Studies at the University of North Texas. He spent many years as a newspaper, radio and television editorialist, and his column, "Texas Sketches," appears weekly in *The Dallas Morning News*.